F, M or Other

Quarrels with the Gender Binary

an anthology from

Knight Errant Press

Edited by Nathaniel Kunitsky and Rhiannon Tate

× 2018 ×

First published in digital and softback in 2018 by
Knight Errant Press
Falkirk, Scotland

© Knight Errant Press 2018

knighterrantpress.com

ISBN 9781999671303

Typeset by Knight Errant Press

Printed in Norfolk by Biddles

This book was curated, edited and assembled by
Nathaniel Kunitsky, Lenka Murová,
Kanika Praharaj and Rhiannon Tate
at Knight Errant Press.

Cover artwork (internal and external), design and graphic
illustrations by Alice Carnegie (Allolune), Rhiannon Tate
and Paul Wilson (Original Cinn) respectively.

Identifying
Challenging Content

We're not only publishers – but human beings, so we know that some content can be quite challenging to take in, especially for an anthology dealing with topics as sensitive as gender identity, experiences of the body, intimacy, sexuality, growing up and how we might see the future unfolding.

As we have assembled this volume, we did our best to identify content that might be considered challenging by what we hope to be a wide variety of readers, with various levels of understanding of the subject matter. We have used a simple graphic to point these pieces out so that they may be approached with caution, or at least with a prepared mindset.

Contents

Contributor Map

North & South America

UK, Europe & Asia

Thank you.

This book was made for you.

Extra special shiny thanks go to the following humans for their generosity:

Jamie Graham, Sara Davis and Greg Shocklee.

The Knight Errant team and our authors extend heartfelt gratitude to all the wonderful humans who have supported us, through the crowdfunding process and otherwise, and who have kick-started this anthology into being.

We would also like to thank our family, partners and friends for putting up with us this year in all our publishing-related frenzy.

Foreword

This anthology (and, later in the year, its companion volume) represent a full years' work from the Knight Errant team. From those early foundations and bringing our tiny publishing house together, we have experienced an incredible journey. Gathering content for an anthology on such a prescient topic as gender, whilst simultaneously building a community interest company, running workshops, meeting new faces and making new connections – has required our Knights to cross frontiers, explore new territories and even, on some occasions, battle a few dragons.

Yet here we stand triumphant, and one Kickstarter campaign later, we present our very first publication – a collection of prose, poetry, comics and everything in between. #QueerQuarrels explores the topic of gender from fresh and varied perspectives, not only from a wide variety of gender identities and communities, but also from across the world.

We have made films together, recorded poetry performances, had live sessions, developed writing skills and confidence in workshops, supported charities and contributed to panels. We've worked closely with our authors to develop their content whilst preserving their voices and styles, and taken care with poetry layouts to retain the pace and energy of live performance. We've blogged, blagged and bantered our way through a year of significant social and political upheaval and are proud of the work that we, our collaborators and contributors have achieved. Half-way through production and in an effort to expand our reach and provide further opportunities for minority writers, we have taken on a dedicated BAME officer.

But let's be clear in our mission: it isn't perfect and, even with the best intentions, there is more work to be done. As a company and as people, we have grown immeasurably, but as with all things, there is always room for improvement. This anthology is simply a selection of voices – a mere scribble in the history of conversation on the topic. We hope it inspires people to question, research, express and, at the very least, feel more comfortable and confident speaking about the subject of gender.

Difficult decisions had to be made regarding placing of content whilst managing our audience's expectations and staying true to our commitment to freedom of expression. We would like to alert readers that some essays contain potentially triggering content and to ensure you are aware before you start reading – the work in question is marked with a content warning symbol. Though every effort has been made to make the writing accessible, we would like to clarify that 'cis' and 'cisgendered' are terms used in some essays to distinguish people who do not identify as trans and/or non-binary. We considered creating a glossary for these terms but decided instead to trust our readers and the power of research.

This book is just a single facet of the fantastic work that has been achieved by our collaborators and contributors. Our Knights will continue to press forward and, in volume two, we hope to wrangle together even more splendid and representative content from across the world, and Scotland, for you to enjoy.

Along with everyone who supported the Kickstarter and helped spread the word about us and the project through social media, we also have a number of people and organisations we would like to thank directly – without their unwavering support and camaraderie we wouldn't have made it this far!

Leanne Kahn at Dalry Open Film (Edinburgh, Scotland) for providing her filming expertise for our Kickstarter and our first ever poetry film *The Body Never Forgets* by Jonathan Bay; LGBT Health & Wellbeing charity for doing the work that they do and supporting us at our launch; Lighthouse Bookshop for being a hub for discourse and a queer haven, and for letting us take over their premises for our launch night; *DIVA* Magazine for giving us a chance and a scintillating first review – and last but not least to Monstrous Regiment, 3 of Cups Press and Scottish Book Trust for sticking by us and spreading the good word on Twitter.

Thank you.

Dear reader, this book is intense.

Hold tight.

We hope you enjoy the journey.

Nathaniel and Rhiannon

May 2018

GENDER*

your box is invisible
or mythical
or just not here at all

so here's another box
a one-size-fits-all
"other" box

climb in

*compulsory information,
select one option.

Gray Crosbie

HAZMAT ROMANCE

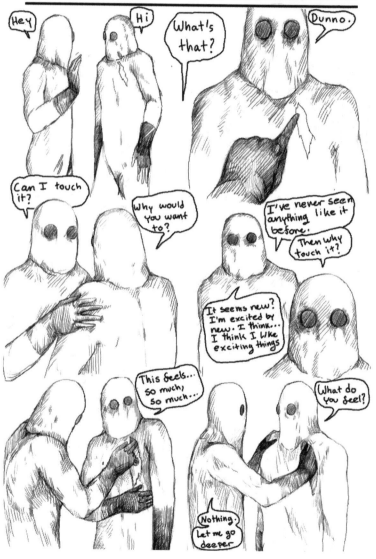

Laura Nicholson

Necessary Monsters

Robert Stirrups

May, 1996

It happened in maths class; it was completely unprovoked. I had never even said anything unpleasant to him. Brian and I lived in completely separate universes, bound by mutual disdain but no outright hostility. The teacher had popped out for a moment and I had started chatting to Laura, who sat in front of me. She was beautiful and so cool it hurt; she had eyes the colour of the Windows 95 start-up screen and liked all the best bands at least a month before me. I was trying to convince her that hating Kula Shaker was a moral imperative rather than mere opinion when Brian casually leaned over and drew a penis on my work. The biro lines were deep and blue, like scars in the paper. It was crude and hairless, with balloons of semen rising from the tip as if from the children's birthday party of the damned. I didn't even see him do it, I only saw Laura's attention wander and the bemused, half-suppressed smile on her face. The teacher returned before I could say or do anything.

He did the same thing the next day, and the next, and the next. I asked him about it but he said he was just messing around. It's all in fun, can't you take a joke?

I wouldn't have minded so much if he hadn't done it in

front of her. That was what made it so humiliating. That was what made it such a violation. It started to bother me so much so that I even started to dream about it.

***

Maths class. Laura was in rapt attention as I expounded on Placebo's musical lineage: "Lydia Lunch begat Sonic Youth, whose LP Sister is..." Brian penised me again. My rage was righteous. I drew a sword and thrust it through his eye. The class cheered, including the teacher.

Laura fluttered her eyelashes. "I knew you were wise – but I didn't realise how fearsomely masculine you were as well! Kiss me, please!"

As I did so, I saw another Laura appear behind her with her hands on her hips.

"This dream sequence is silly! Come on! You can't fight him. He's bigger than you, and if you say anything he'll just make out you're a big square who can't take a joke. The only way to win is not to play."

"But I have to do something!"

"You're smarter than him. You've seen how he struggles with quadratic equations! Figure out why he's doing it and you'll figure out how to win. But hurry! With every penis he draws, the real Laura will increasingly see you as a figure of contempt and then you'll never be able to ask me out!"

I woke up in a cold panic.

Dream-Laura's question haunted me all through the next day. Why do guys like Brian need to humiliate others? Why do they need to dominate people? Why bring his knob into it? In a flash, I saw Brian's unsolicited ink-cocks as a microcosm of male sexual violence. Was it an act of symbolic rape? What motivates someone to put a cock where they know it would not be welcomed? How does an organ meant for procreation and love become a weapon?

Are Brians born or are they made? Who teaches them to act like that, to think like that, and to feel like that?

***

I dreamt I was a draftee in a war movie. A drill sergeant marched up and down, sneering and barking. I was holding a bayonet and a row of dummies was lined up in front of us, all sculpted to look like supermodels.

"I am here to turn you into a soldier! A living weapon! Don't you know we are at war?! The first rule of war is: KNOW YOUR ENEMY!" He handed me a folder with 'KNOW YOUR ENEMY' stencilled on the front. Inside it was a lingerie catalogue.

"This is just a…" I started.

"The enemy long to dehumanise the warrior! To women we are nothing but gamete factories! We must hate them as they hate us! They must fear us as we fear them!"

"Wait… what?"

"A warrior is always angry! A warrior knows nothing

but eternal rage! A warrior ends every sentence with an exclamation mark! A warrior channels his anger and uses it against the enemy! What makes you angry?!"

The answer came as if by magic.

"The fact that I'm not allowed to express any emotion other than rage, sir! I am a complex human being capable of a variety of drives and responses! My basic emotional needs are unfulfilled and I am prohibited by society from expressing my grief at this state of affairs!"

The sergeant beamed.

"Good work soldier! That is a battle cry to be proud of! Charge!"

"I have a rich and complex inner life that requires respect and validation!" I screamed as I plunged my bayonet into an effigy of Kate Moss.

***

Wednesday. Chemistry. My favourite subject, but only because Laura was my lab partner. She was talking about some film but I couldn't stop thinking about Brian's penis. I wanted to ask her out but how could I with the cock of Damocles hanging over my head?

"It's called Twelve Monkeys. Directed by one of the Pythons. Something about a mental patient trying to stop the apocalypse."

That was why I liked her so much – not just her looks or

anything but because she got so excited about the same things I did. I wanted to ask her out so much but how could I until I dealt with Brian? Didn't she realise how much I wanted to ask her out? But she just kept going on about this damned film!

"I'd like to see it sometime. It's out this weekend." She sounded like there was something else she wanted to say but Mrs. Phillister interrupted and we spent the next hour thinking about esters instead.

***

I dreamt I was in MFI looking at couches with Sigmund Freud. I held a booklet of fabric swatches up for him; he seemed quite taken with a petunia print.

"Dr. Freud, why do men fear and hate women?"

The founder of psychoanalysis puffed on his pipe and sat down on a hot pink futon.

"The small boy spends his whole day surrounded by women, his mother or his nursemaid, each of whom exerts enormous power over him. He doesn't understand why she screams to stop when he climbs on the sideboard or runs out towards the busy road. To him, she must seem like the most arbitrary dictator. But he loves her and needs her to survive. He learns that the main difference between these necessary monsters and himself is the inch of flesh between his legs. Now he has an explanation; a means to make sense of all this. Perhaps the mother resents the boy for his wholeness and wants to make him into a deformed freak like herself."

Freud lay down upon a leopard print futon, testing it out, but then shook his head.

"For boys like Brian masculinity is a state of permanent crisis; you must always be on guard against anything that will make you feel small and weak. You must obey those stronger than you rather than risk standing up to them and losing. Women exist primarily as markers of a man's success and as a prize for men to fight over, devoid of thoughts or desires of their own. Brian is locked inside his own defences; he must be very lonely in there."

I woke up in a frenzy of compassion. Brian was not to be loathed or defeated. He was to be helped and healed. I hit upon a plan of action, and set to work.

***

Maths class. I smiled at Brian.

"I wanted to thank you for your gift. I didn't understand before but now I do."

He squinted, puzzled.

"All those sketches of your penis! Thank you for sharing your penis with me."

He squinted again, like he was confused, or possibly about to cry.

"I understand now! It was an act of intimacy and vulnerability but I wasn't ready for that intimacy. I want to tell you that your penis is beautiful. You need to be acknowledged as a sexual being. Brian. I acknowledge you. Guys don't get to be sexual objects; don't get to feel adored the way girls do. We need to be desired. You hid that desire in an act of aggression but I understand! I want to show you something."

I reached into my bag and got out a dozen of his dick pics, now mounted on cardboard and laminated.

Laura turned round and watched silently, puzzled, smirking.

"I treasure your gift," I said, "and I want to share my penis with you too."

I reached into my bag and handed him a portrait of my genitals; a carefully rendered sketch in fine HB pencil. It too was laminated.

I pushed it across the desk to him and, not knowing how to respond, he slid it into his pocket. A moment later class began.

Brian never drew a penis on my classwork again.

KNEES

Gray Crosbie

when she falls
and grazes shins
skin deep
on that shard of glass
camouflaged
grass green

and hiccups sobs
from her knees
she hears them say:

boys play rough

you're asking for trouble

it will all end in tears

Shrinking Violence

Harry Mason

I'm sitting here and I've been hungry for over an hour but I'm not eating. I wrote this sentence, and then I pulled myself up and went to get something to eat. This is what recovery looks like, for me at least. It doesn't look like nothing ever happened. It doesn't look like a steady soft upwards curve towards perfectly normal. It looks like gradual, stilted progress; some days I am still paralysed with panic as I try to choose something to eat, but some days now, I enjoy a meal without even thinking about it. Some days I still look in the mirror and feel shudders of disgust at this body; but some days now, I catch a glimpse of my reflection in a shop window and I am pleasantly surprised to find my own self smiling back.

It's never really been about weight for me. Weight is a red herring – it's about masculinity. I never had a problem with weight until my body began to betray me, bulging and bleeding and breaking apart from who I am. My bones stopped short, my shoulders were stunted, my voice left high and dry. I begged my body to grow right; push ups and pull ups, sweating and aching to try and earn the shape which other boys were just waking up to, like a shiny fifty pence piece under their dinosaur print pillows. That's when hunger came into the picture. I couldn't be bigger, not in the right ways, so I would have to be smaller.

But smaller didn't help either. I was clicking and dragging at the corner of my self image, and no matter what size I pulled myself into the shape – the problem – would not change. Even when my clothes hung loose from my frame, when a partner recoiled at my ribcage stretching my skin thin, my chest sagged with tissue that made me feel sick and my hips were humiliating.

My body is unrecognisable from the one that betrayed me when I was a child. Living there made my skin crawl, and so I crawled out of my skin and searched for something to shield my raw flesh from the air. I paid tribute to oracles, I ingested potent tinctures, I sacrificed a calf to the gods, I ached through trial after trial. And here I stand – bloody but unbowed. Women are tormented by the virgin/whore dichotomy – they mustn't be prudes, they mustn't be sluts, they must live to indulge men's libidinous drives, they mustn't allow their beautiful delicate flower to be trampled. It's a trick question – designed to catch you out, to leave you feeling foolish and vulnerable; you misunderstood, you're not supposed to get it right. Before I even understood myself as a man, I was subject to a different trick question – make your body big and strong enough to scoop up your damsel, fight for your country, protect your family but you mustn't make the mistake of being chubby or doughy or bulky. Fat is womanly – men's bodies are made of bone and muscle and skin. My insecurities are in a constant battle to make me both bigger and smaller at once. This isn't technically impossible – body builders employ 'bulking and cutting' to live up to this paradoxical masculine ideal, to be huge and powerful but also slim, cut, ripped. Of course they can't win either – they're too much, they're grotesque, they're vain.

And even if I dedicated hours of my life to achieving the correct shape, the correct body fat percentage, the correct tightrope masculine balance of big and small – one of the key ingredients of ideal masculinity is comically out of my reach – I cannot make myself tall. Again, this isn't impossible – there are surgeons who will literally break your legs to make you two inches closer to tall, dark, and handsome. Men are breaking their bones to be bigger and starving themselves to be smaller. This image of masculinity is so restrictive it trips over itself leaving no satisfactory option, no winners.

Recovery has gradually, quietly given me an alternative image of what it means to be a man. I feel masculine when I teach my brother how to use a safety razor. I feel masculine when I look down at my strong furry thighs. I feel masculine when I take care of my wife by cleaning the house. I feel masculine when I realise that when you define masculinity for yourself, it transforms from a fragile contradiction into an expansive discovery.

Drag Hag

Fee Johnstone

Her telephone shrilled indignantly and on the other end she heard Arthur's mollifying tone, "Someone to see you, Mrs Bond." Before Mrs Bond had the chance to adjust her satin blouse after an impromptu rearrangement of her new push-up bra, in walked a long, lank, miserable streak of beige. The gender-indeterminate person who drooped before her was her new client – and although Mrs Bond had been expecting her, she was still taken aback by the lacklustre demeanour and equally uninspiring attire presented before her.

"Ah Deborah! I'm delighted to see you!" exclaimed Mrs Bond, proffering her hand to the expressionless shape. "You said you could help me?" her new client mumbled through lips resembling enthusiastically-rolled modelling clay. "Of course, my dear, let me explain," said Mrs Bond, looking Deborah over from her brown scuffed sandals to her limp ashen hair. The face bore no makeup nor any sign of ever having lived through anything more thrilling than an accidental secretion of bodily gas in a public space.

Mrs Bond enlightened Deborah as to the nature of the exclusive makeover service she offered. You see, this was not your average makeover service; she didn't simply assist women with the odd styling issue, she actually refashioned those introverted, invisible women into flamboyant and fabulous drag queens: drag queens the world believed to have been born with male appendage. Of course, her business was shrouded in secrecy because this was a profession that men were not yet ready to relinquish to women – they wanted to keep the fluffy stilettos and feather boas to themselves.

The females who used her services were usually those dowdy, solitary types who wore misshapen clothing to disguise what lurked beneath, dressing in muted colours lest anyone notice them. But, underneath the sacking and half-masts, was a desire for something more from life.

Mrs Bond herself had been one of those frumpy females until her late teenage years.

She'd always been freakishly tall with cumbersome feet, and that she wore her dad's loafers was a constant source of ridicule. But the day she was drafted in to play the school's pantomime dame (because no one else had the build to carry off the kaftan designed for a giant), was the best day of her life. Astonishingly, she found that on stage she could be someone else, that she needed no script to be sarcastic and scathing. Although she'd been made up to look like a disfigured clown, she knew that this was who she wanted to be. She'd dress up only in private and over the years, she discarded the stripy tights and comedy shoes and evolved from Widow Twanky into one of the world's most famous drag queens. But the years were not kind to those ungainly feet she'd been wedging into dainty shoes. She was forced to retire early after a series of falls, one of which nearly exposed her (literally) as a woman. Instead, she turned her attentions to helping other women clinch highly coveted drag queen roles. So successful was she at her makeovers that unbeknownst to most, many of the world's top drag artists were capable of birthing more than just an alter ego. Only she, her loyal employee Arthur – and of course her 'Creations' – were privy to this information. Mrs Bond christened her clients 'Creations' because they were her works of art; with each transformation she created a new life: a life that would ultimately be filled with silicon and venom and cabaret.

Owing to the clandestine nature of the business, Mrs Bond alone was responsible for recruiting Creations. Arthur, who had been living in the shadow of Mrs Bond's array of stupendous wigs from the outset, found her methods of stalking those with promise rather creepy, but he marvelled at how accurately she could identify the next 'Poly Ester' or 'Breasty Betsy'.

She'd spot them on the bus lost in romantic fiction, hiding behind the bulk of their fellow passengers, or alone in museums staring adoringly at a Cleopatra bust, wishing they had the pluck to wear a winged headdress. Once she had her taupe target, Mrs Bond would ingratiate herself into their lives, gain their trust and woo them with tales of the sensational life that could be theirs. She would only divulge her line of work once she was certain they would agree and that they would keep the secret.

Following the big reveal, the women became her willing students without hesitation and the initial self-consciousness of removing their ill-fitting robes would vanish as soon as their skin felt the itch and scratch of their new tutu. They'd spin around in graceless circles and often attempt moves well beyond their inflexible reach, ignoring the chafe of synthetic material against orifices more accustomed to lightweight linen.

Mrs Bond delighted in the moment they would look in the mirror for the first time; the shock of seeing themselves as an exceptionally gaudy yet feminine woman was so overwhelming that it brought tears, fainting and, on one unfortunate occasion, urination.

Aesthetics aside, the most challenging aspect of her job was teaching the women to be women. These were women who had spent their lives in flat-soled shoes being as innocuous as possible and now they were expected to be utterly preposterous, strut in heels and feign laughter. If they could master that, they could indeed be the lead drag queen at any club they wished – without anyone knowing what junk they carried in their trunk.

For thirty years, she and her Creations gained notoriety for the most ingenious costumes, the most acerbic yet amusing insults and the most amount of hairspray second only to the musical. Mrs Bond revelled in her own success, expelling money like glitter with champagne baths, hand-stitched bodystockings and naturally, her own personal podiatrist to tend to those feet.

Life may have been a lie carefully crafted out of callousness and calluses but she basked in every hair-flip, every contoured cheekbone and every newly-manufactured, confident female who could make one's entire viscera quiver with one look.

But everything changed when she met Deborah. Mrs Bond, usually so devoid of all compassion, had spotted Deborah ferrying a cat around in a papoose and pitied the poor woman. She felt her heart ache as Deborah explained with a twinkle in her eye that the cat was her soulmate – her only mate. Judgement clouded by emotion, Mrs Bond forwent her usual investigative routine and immediately offered her life-changing service to Deborah. And now, here she was, this soft-spoken lummox of a woman, shedding cat hair as though it were her own.

The transformation did not go well; Deborah appeared to lack a capable hand with which to dress herself. That her skin repelled all cosmetics should have been the slap in Mrs Bond's rouged face that was needed to cease the charade, but she persisted – a papoose-wearing cat lady would not be her first failure. Regardless of the seemingly insurmountable issues, Mrs Bond sent Deborah (now going by the moniker 'Deplorable De-bore-ah') out into the world, hoping with time she'd be the drag hag of Mrs Bond's technicoloured dreams. Arthur, her only ally, had bravely attempted an intervention but was swatted away as though he were but an errant fly seeking adventure in her false eyelashes.

Deborah was forgetful and would often turn up for drag auditions squeezed into diamante hotpants but having omitted to shave her legs. She was unable to colour-match, her wigs resembled imploded cupcakes and she could not improvise when her putdowns failed to muster a sneer. Each audition was worse than the previous and her lack of ability to play the part was threatening to compromise the whole operation. It was only a matter of time before Deborah's failures would draw attention to Mrs Bond, raising questions of her anatomy. This could not be allowed to happen! No one could ever know that she, Drag Queen of the World 1987, was born with real flesh and blood breasts, albeit ones so small you'd be forgiven for thinking she was standing with her back to you. Imagine how the drag queen community would turn on her if they knew that no inch of her was prosthetic! They'd feel betrayed and insulted. She'd be the punchline to the jokes she had created. They'd uncover pictures of her wearing a fawn jumpsuit, they'd find out that her real name was Brenda Brown!

But, she had no one else to blame but herself; of course she thought she could make a success of dear, docile Deborah, even when defeat and dishevelment were staring her in the face. How could she have gotten it so wrong? Rumination and ruination aside, deep down she knew what was happening and had to finally admit why she had been so uncharacteristically ruled by the very emotions she had stuffed away into her bra as a teenager: Mrs Bond was menopausal. The wicked outbursts were favourable in this profession but the bouts of depression, the endless tears and having to wear adult nappies to catch the unfortunate leakages were quite another. That she was also now struggling to keep control of her recently acquired facial hair was most unsettling and quite unbecoming of a woman supposedly as ladylike as she. When the first crop appeared, like a dusting of hungry ants, she cleverly metamorphosed into a Geisha Girl, which allowed for heavy makeup and a fan as a constant companion but as the facial fur burgeoned into something resembling a backcombed merkin, it no longer became possible to mask.

So, there was nothing else for it. Unless she wanted to be internationally humiliated and disgraced she would need to depart from this sparkly yet abrasive world of femininity. As she felt her life's work sashay off before her rheumy eyes, she could no longer stand to look at this façade of a person she had fabricated. Dejectedly, she flung her wig to the ground in a cloud of talcum powder. She relinquished her forgiving Jimmy Choos (custom-made to accommodate her generous trotters) and peeled off her dress. Aided by ethanol and a brillo pad she scrubbed at her face until all evidence that Mrs Bond, Drag Queen Extraordinaire, had been erased. She baulked at her reflection, her wide set jaw all the more pronounced now that her graduated bob no longer shaped her face. She wept and winced as she flattened the wiry hairs that sprouted in patches from her chest like petrified threadworms.

She was broken. All she had known for the last thirty years was tiaras, triumph and transformation. And Arthur. Her heart descended into the pile of discarded clothes as she realised she'd have to let him go. Good old Arthur, as faithful as acne to pubescent skin, as reliant as Robin. But what was he without her? He had devoted over half his life to Mrs Bond and her Creations, dutifully awaiting his orders and adhering to her every whim. He knew nothing else, she thought, as she picked up the phone to summon him.

He entered the room giving her a woeful look, and if he was surprised to see her as plain and pallid Brenda, his face did not betray him. But before a word could pass her trembling lips, he removed his shirt and hung it over her bare shoulders, threading her lifeless arms into the sleeves and buttoning it over her little lychee lumps. He then took off his trousers and she allowed him to guide her mottled stumps into the legs, feeling some warmth and dignity return. "Thank you, Arthur," she murmured gratefully but he shushed her gently. He wasn't finished. He turned up the collar of the shirt and nimbly adorned her with his silk paisley tie before taking his comb to her unruly fringe and sweeping it back. With a spritz of Old Spice he beamed at her and left the room with a wink to attend to the distantly ringing doorbell (and perhaps to re-robe himself). After he closed the door, she glanced down at her new attire with bafflement and dared to look again at her reflection. But this time, as the tears dispersed from her eyes, she gasped and a smile crept across her handsome face.

She had barely time to twirl her moustache with her own spittle when her telephone shrilled indignantly and on the other end she heard Arthur's mollifying tone, "Someone to see you, Mr Bond."

The Body Is...

Nic Lachance

body and shower head

when i masturbate with the shower head, i go somewhere else. i am at a dinner table with floating sentences. the shower head strums in the background to softly spoken lemon tea, yellow bundles, barely faced melted torsos. barely body because their warmth melts chest cavities, trachea and spines. they twist your fingernails with their forgiveness. take away all that hardness.

they have a face that used to be mine but is now just something else. float. residue of cheek and skin and forehead with only curled smiles and my own eyes. at first, my cunt doesn't want to meet them. we are afraid and want to fantasise about old boyfriends instead – the ones who never made me cum but chaffed enough on the sides of my insides to make me think feeling burn was the same as feeling pleasure. but these things, this ancient citrus, they hold onto to the tips of me. they reassure my shakes.

we introduce ourselves: i am the earth body that is living out trauma and mundane disappointments. they are the collection of every prayer ever said. they tell me that they are the old, dusty mothers of me. they are home. they are the wool doll that sits in the stem of my coat pocket telling me what to keep and what to let die; which grocery store to pick up soy milk at and whether or not i should visit the sea this morning. they laugh around me as the shower head wastes away. i am still wasting hot water. still thinking about what parts of me run down the drain.

they drum against me. my body tastes goodness. this buzz up and down my legs, forcing its way in the insides of my thighs, this is for me. not the me in the shower but the me i have been chasing since i have been stolen from myself.

my clitoris meets the running of water with teeth, with the sponge tissue of my g-spot strums. i tighten to these voices, these dusty mothers. i feel all the nettles and twisted dandelions sprout out of my cunt and sprawl. they cut me. memories swell around me and me in nonverbal hymns, i cum only when the plants and angels and scars shake my jaw hard enough to make me agree (and never forget) that i am worth fighting for.

what do you do when all your tears have dried and can no longer fall from your eye sockets so you become cry. they find bubble and wetness between your toes, they fill up your forearm, your throat becomes full of cry and tears and salty becomings.

they hold me. they shout me all the niceties i want so badly to be true. they say: LET ME IN

do you hear me?

you,

half

québecois,

half raped

half-way home:

do want

to love

again?

HE WAS WRONG

push my fingers down your throat

guilt is a three-legged chair you can't rock on anymore

you haven't tasted yourself since

he took your

salt

YOU ARE MADE OF LOVE

can you help me:

make

alive?

you deserve pleasure;

they are the ones who told me i am enough, i am not always woman, barely even gendered at all. they told me i can hold my body gently again; that my gender is somewhere between healing and the salty top layer of the sea.

now i wait. after i cum and hold hands with the teachers in my chest, i wait to feel again.

body and vibrator

when i was 18 i bought my first vibrator. it was purple and had a frail cord running between the remote and the tangerine-sized bud. i spent hours making myself cum, laughing and howling in the creases of my bedroom. i was so obsessed with making my own body cum that i never wanked without bringing snacks into bed with me: bananas, chocolate, ginger nut cookies, nutella, nature valley granola bars, pink lady apples, ice cream, snickers. it was dizzying.

i felt queer in the most profound way i could feel queer.

queer because i needed nothing but batteries and my own body to feel something. no script or performance; no man with jurisdiction over my sounds, my mountains or my orgasms. the tombs of my moans were mine.

no more the days of dull compulsive heterosexual dance to

recite because my hands were on my own thighs, my own quivering.

i would invite a bootycall at 3A.M every saturday night named Connor and make him watch me cum. he had a massive dick and red hair and was less flesh and mostly skeleton but we sucked each other broken until weird hours of the night. he could watch and touch himself, only when i said he could. i would get completely lost in my own body and in the growing erection across the bed from me. don't touch yourself. not yet. it was my first taste of a domination/submission relationship but was problematic because i was/am drenched in trauma and internalised misogyny and was a power-deprived trauma survivor dominating a boy in love with being loved. he would just watch me wiz away on this vibrator. and i would get lost, uninterested in his erection and pleasure and what to do with his dick. the vibrator let me find my own multiplicity. it let me translate the languages of my cunt and understand magicmagicmagic.

vibrators gave me trans fantasies: i fucked people with this ghost penis, my face morphed into other faces, i embodied a cis gay man, i embodied cunt and sun and hard femme and boy and spirit. i allowed myself to replace the brown, overgrown fingernails that i let cut the riffs of my cunt with vibrating velvet, purple dream, soft machine murmur.

body and body

my body has imprints all over it. your fingers, his forearm.

your bleached teeth. all the stains of trauma i never needed. sometimes i think everyone knows exactly what my trauma looks like and where it is in me because once in a while, their fingers will graze over it or they will speak at it and all my stains will come back to life again.

and the stains, they smell so bad. like smoked out nettles we burn after a day of gardening, rinsed in petrol, marinated in the pisswatershowercum bucket of recycled water we keep to water our garden. other days they smell like imposter and plastic. or like the sour wafts from the white, inedible and bitter rind of a lemon.

i guess my body is still afraid. i wonder if i just have to just have to wait it out. if there is no thing to wait out for but only the process of becoming, of being kinder, of tending softer hands to myself.

the other day i was thinking that maybe my healing is like soup.

it starts as blank water and it only feels like there are foreign bits floating in you.

just as water, damp celery/bay leaf/oregano/pepper/ carrot/potato/marjoram, all these ingredients simmering at odds with each other. you are nothing but the fighting of all these different things. they bite for space. the oregano wants it to be oregano soup, the celery to be celery soup.

but you wait. it boils. it takes time and heat. and one day, everything is a bit softer. all the things you didn't want to own you, don't own you anymore. the green vegetables become the water and the water becomes coloured. you taste again. maybe you even taste good again. eventually you boil the peripheries of each single thing and they find something completely different. they become different, a fresh intersection of each other.

somehow you make it out of whatever sandpaper corner you were stuck in, abused in, made tiny in, and then you have to wait for yourself to come back. you have to empty the cavities and lungs and even the wet spaces under your fingernails of that old grey water, bit by bit, day by day, and to let the colours soak back in. some days it will rain in your soup again or your palm will moisten from nothing and you will have to go back underwater. but you will keep going. there is no other way, really.

let the colours in, child.

your body wants your calm.

your body wants you to rest and receive all the compliments (as if they weren't the hardest thing to hear)

it wants to feel when you fuck, feel when it becomes rusty morning and laugh when there is something to laugh about.

it wants to feel. it just wants to feel.

my feet dangle on forehead,

over the pole of my head and the flattening of my hair.

sprawled.

my toes touch each other,

my knees on the floor.

i swear when i am folded over like this, doing my secret problematic white person yoga in

my bedroom with floor space just long enough for a rolled out yoga mat, my body tells me stories.

my lower back tells me to trust, trust, trust the way the sun will feed you.

and when i push my shoulders against themselves, they cry out in shame.

like the younger versions of me are itching, backflip of my torso.

it feels like traumas are squeezing themselves through me, out of me, inside of me.

and when i finish, i cry dry tears with no water in them, dry heaving.

seeing flashes of all the queertransfamily that loves me, of the mom that loves me, of trans papa who lets me talk about my birth chart and gives me advice on how to ask one of my partners if we can use a strap-on together.

when i move my body i swear i am given a second chance to know it again. like my dry cries make for slick cement pavements i can roll down on july evenings with a bicycle and no helmet. like i can go free.

i think about the femme who stepped on my heart only to put it back together again. the femme who tapped my clit in the morning like taptaptap and cupped the sweat of my lower back. who i read a poem to that said you are the femme who can step on my heart and put it back together. how scary is it to say to someone you love that they can ruin you.

how do you thank the femme for meeting you in this space of antiquity. of notime and lifetimes. of spinach queer silence. of soul food. how do you thank the femme who kisses you so soft, so burgundy lipstick, so open lipped. so quiet you feel them melt over you, biting the tops of your teeth.

bite me.

i ask you to bite my nipples harder only because i have always dreamed of being on your bottom lip,

bitten against your mouth all the time. moving when you talk, holding to your brittle ends.

have you ever dreamed of being bottom lip to anyone?

body and prayer

i never want to admit that my genders carry stains with them; that they are actually a pile of ash and water and shards and little girl grief and rejection. that one of my stages of non-binary are a kind of dying of a lot of my old selves, from the brokenness of abuse, from vacant parents. all the bad that has claimed a corner of my now gender. i don't want to tell anyone that i am non-binary because woman was not for me: it gave me little black dresses and made me shrink until i was nothing. that my 'they' pronouns have been dragged through men trying to fuck me like a hole, like deadened ash, like nothing, all while i wondered how sex is supposed to do anything but rupture you. non-binary because the binary violated me, because my gender was for an expensive museum exhibit everyone goes to but never admits to not understanding. and really, the real secret i never want to tell, is that there was no place left in my gender for all my infinities.

my prayer tonight is

of crumpled forgiveness letters on my altar

my prayer is a plot twist: it turns out i matter

abusers were wrong, parents too hurt to reach me, gender too busy

building boxes and wrong punctuation,

it turns out the sea doesn't sting when you open your eyes in it

and that love doesn't hurt only the shit we put around it

my prayer tonight is the breadmaker i set overnight, the

prayer as weird dreams about flat bread, flat bread anxiety, flatness and other inadequacies manifesting through breadmaking, wake up at 6A.M because you are worried about the bread and the bread rose perfectly, has seeds and bubbles of yeast on the inside and all

my prayer tonight is for my dad who is too gay and french and wounded and man to admit to any of these things

my prayer tonight is the three hour phone calls with mom, after divorce and never ordering potatoes or beige foods, twenty four years after her cunt birthed trauma, it is survivorship stories, it is the way our prayers have started and ended in the same way this whole time

my prayer tonight is feeding the queertrans housing co-op, my amen is the way they are quiet with food, slapping, lip smacking, you fed them, hallelujah is your own hands you fed them and even if there is carrot peel under your fingernails and you swore nineteen times when the garlic spit back at you you fucking fed them

my prayer is my letting my gender die and being born on the other side

my prayer tonight is

to you capricorn moon, deep feelers, headspace neurotic virgo healers,

you always sad girl, cheer up girl, you still thinking about space girl

to the ones who have felt like they are always too much.
like all the doorframes

of buildings are too tight to hold you in them.

my prayer is for everyone who has been told,

in the quietest ways: you are too much.

my prayer tonight is

dear xe, I AM SCARED

my prayer tonight

is a shower head

that whispers that

my body will taste again

pressed up against my cunt

shake my cheeks

am i enough yet am i enough yet am i enough yet

my prayer tonight

is changing every name headlining the love letters

i've written with

with the names of all my younger selves

my prayer tonight is saying no

until you don't love me for my yes anymore

my prayer tonight is for the starbucks barista

who has two codes for the bathrooms: one for

women, one for men, i'm sorry you have

to give everyone the wrong code. i'm sorry

they make you police us, especially the confusing ones

my prayer tonight is for everyone to feel

like they matter so they are just valid

body and re-membering

at the rainbow synth gay club last friday

filled with white cis gay men,

you dance back.

you dance reminded.

to a time when you were 6 and asked

all the adults at the party are you happy but they were

too drunk to get it so they pinched

your cheeks closed.

(but quiet me won't give you quiet, baby)

back into every pink lace dream you had while you lie at
19 beside the stoner boyfriend who fucks you in the wrong
place without asking and you are too soft from the bong to
correct him. but when you are both sober and he still fucks
you in the wrong place without asking, you wonder why
love to him means silencing you.

while he sleeps 19 year-old weed dreams beside you,

you fantasise about killing him and marrying his sister.

instead you close your eyes and

make love with the future

see:

a pixie femme harp player you would meet

4 years later who taught you how to fuck

against a bunk bed and

stick around.

a dark haired healer who lets you wet her chest with your

feelings. who teaches you that your neck is

for laughing, not just carrying.

a queer mechanic you learned how to love

over basement punk bands and animal collective,

whose lower back stains

your bedsheets and notebooks.

the non-binary who sees past your performance and who
fists you

until your body knows pleasure again.

you see everything before it comes.

but that is your secret to keep

keep pretending you didn't see all of your becoming before
they come.

keep pretending that you don't see queer futures – all your
futures – sprawled and canvassed over the backs of your
eye lids.

right now, you cannot have any of this.

you are 19 and need to finish your philosophy degree and get high on friday and keep pretending.

keep pretending that you aren't waiting for the moment when you are 24 and you make a facebook status to all your family and liberal friends to tell them you are trans. that you always have been trans. that you have always been girl/ not girl/un-girl/de-girl in the same body. that before you could shave the bottom half of your head, you have had a conceptual undercut since you were 12. you have always been here, you just never felt the girls' change room was safe enough to say it so you just waited to leave this place. so you just waited to find your queer baptism.

so even when you are slouched over his dirty checkered bedsheets, so small in yourself you are crumb against pillow, even when you are 19 and fissured and so high, so cis and straight to everyone looking in, still dating the least organised drug dealer in east ottawa:

you see everything.

Equations to integrate along a gender curve

Jonathan Bay

brave and outlandish,
in front of the mirror
derivative rules exclude
what a trans* person should wear
to a drag party

no one teaches these identity functions

factorial of borrowed items:
someone's purple push-up bra
for these shrinking parabolas,
tighty whities overstuffed,
a pink trucker hat from Pahrump, NV,
titty mountains and cherry nips
approaching a slant of infinite limit

the bicycle pack of queers
clatter to wheels,
ties and pasted moustaches
flagging a vector into the darkness

vibrational constants bump music
to harmonic progression
as we empty beer cans
leave glitter curves on the walls

here are the limits of behaviour,
unbelievably a hand gropes breasts
I THOUGHT THEY WERENT REAL!
words slurred and hung,
polynomials blurring the air

not everyone can proof this equation
my exhalation
Lady, just don't grab my tube sock dick.

Slash Fiction

Freddie Alexander

I have seen Clark Kent kiss Bruce
with tongue, naked in the fortress of solitude
save for leather cowl and ball-gag.

He traced a line from pectoral
towards batarang in the cold air
of fan fiction, smut.

This taut, muscular fantasy,
the Dark Knight read in Polari,
some fratboy's nightmare:

sweet and clear water pours over Wolverine's
hairy stomach; Triple H goes down on Shaun
Michaels and Chyna, ribald and ecstasy,

lips clutched pale, hands through velvet clasped,
luxury and ass, you violent men made
quivering flesh and caught gasp.

Androgyny

George McDermid

Is she a he?
I see a she
why fear the he beneath?

She feels a she
she lives a she
it's you I fear
good grief

She is a she
was born a she
despite your own belief

I wish you'd see
all he and she
a single living tree
and each he and she
upon that tree
a multi-coloured leaf

Message to My Fellow Men

Max Scratchmann

Contrary to popular belief, this is what a feminist looks like.

No,
not your typical Doc-Martin-wearing, man-hating,
shaven-headed-dyke-feminazi
who's just queuing up for a damn-good-seeing-to from you
to sort all her delusional ideas out.

No,
this feminist is a stereotype-defying paunchy middle-aged man
who's never read Germaine Greer or Andrea Dworkin
and, quite frankly,
wouldn't know a female eunuch if one jumped up and bit him.

Yes,
this feminist is a balding,
almost vegetarian would-like-to-be vegan if I could only give
up cheese,
herbal-tea-drinking
lost-cause
with an occasional good line
in fart gags.

And I don't have a degree in Gender Studies
and I've never opened a Sociology text book
to check what I should be thinking next
to qualify as a new man,
because,
after all,
my mother and yours created your and my sorry asses
without ever looking at the instruction manual,
moon cycle by moon cycle,
and if that's not a fucking miracle
I don't know what is.

And,
have you even looked at the world around you lately,
and are you
really, seriously,
going to tell me
that you're still interested in playing at domestic tyrants
in the face of corporate-owned governments,
food banks
and
oh
– all those icebergs that are slowly melting away.

Because
there are no such things as Women's Issues
when we're talking about the bigger picture of Human Issues
and the planet's being slowly driven towards self destruction,
and maybe you ought to think about that
before you go out and vote
for the next brainless Neanderthal
that appeals to your caveman instincts.

And do you,
honestly,
still think it's OK
to denigrate half the world's population
just because they don't have cocks?

Because,
let me tell you,
the future is not looking good for your unborn children
right now
and,
when the flood water's creeping slowly up the Forth
and threatening to become a tidal wave any minute,
I don't know what's going to save you,
but it sure as fuck won't be
the size of your balls, that's for certain.

And so it's time to man up
and look into the mirror and say,
this
this
is what a feminist looks like.

Hemingway Masculinity

Sarah Spence

Hemingway masculinity speaks in plain facts.
It does not need
adjectives or adverbs.
It does not need
to explain itself.
It writes objectively.
It declares. It does not need question marks.

Hemingway masculinity is the pen that strikes
through other people's words.

Immaculate Conception

Jonathan Bay

I thought the way I performed
sex made me exempt from miracles.

There was not an angel.
Only our naked bodies
touching,
finding ecstasy
in the curved spaces.
Now the seed is laid
in my male womb.

The gift I carry is precious.
Deep in my belly
each second of growth
confounds my heart;
but in the shadow of the beats
there is fear
like the tick-twitch
of a nervous mouth
shy – leering –
building.

This gift I carry is a secret.
Before it comes to the world,
safe inside,
only I know
that it will be peeled,
onion sleeves,
delicate and spicy,
in words like "Let you without sin
cast the first stone."

This gift I carry is hope.
Worn proudly beneath
this cloth,
touch my angelic stretch marks,
feel the soft kick with your hand.
I am unashamed,
Rub this lotion into my happiness.

This body is my body.
Here is my swollen belly.
Here is my naked joy.
Here is my male womb.
Here is my seed.
Look at my body.

XY

Iliria Osum

I   Helen!   proclaim
    I exist in other mouths but yours.
Twice-stolen and war-avenged, I turn my patience
now to other things. Oh — rent hikes, for example.
You think there's a black market value for such as
my gold apples? My beauty at the least is trans-
actional.

            My mother never wanted me to do as the
Greeks did. She thought them oily. Real men, she
claimed, don't suffer that kind of thing. But suffer
I did. And at last I took the name for myself.

                                        Thus
whose reality? Mine? My mother's? Yours?
    Hardly
yours, Paris. Despite yourself, you've disclaimed
me. Know me as Helen, herself, or unknow me.

Well? How do you like them apples?

                                        Tell me,
with the years behind us now, have you discovered
how one recovers after having been dead?

                                   A cup of wine?

                    A lamb's tongue?

                         A learned ungentleness?

My mother declaimed me Helen, yes, and dead;
I consider myself a breathing creature, and one
who knows that life has no pleasures in it but
what makes the body soft.

    Do you find me soft,
now, or merely clouded by my rosy scent? Imagine
you I was thus anointed for a first coupling?

    No, Paris!
    No, fool!

I   Helen!   acclaim
      myself, in body and in name alike.
Born of an egg, born once again unboy. A
flat-chested child become Helen, ex-Troy.

Hairy On The Inside

Hannah Newell

The Monster, the Mother, the Myth and Medusa

I have volume somewhere inside of me; a reticent capacity for loudness. A deep cackle, full of dirty mirth, occasionally escapes from my terrible, small mouth. I have hated my mouth: a pink leather coin purse clutched in cherubim softness. It's pretty, some say. Or they make lewd jokes about what will or won't fit in it. I see it disappear in fleshy folds when I put on a smile. My lips get thin. Will they roll back completely with age? How far will I have ground down my teeth by then?

My mother contains that same laugh, my aunt as well, and when it escapes this great sound only seems to be at an acceptable volume when intermingling with others, in chorus or cacophony. Otherwise it tends to be simply shocking, to me as much as anyone else; an assault on decency. People look and I feel ashamed. But where it is safe to laugh, where there is pathos, there is such release and joy, such expansion. My teeth feel oh so big inside my small, small mouth. All the better to kiss you with, my dear.

Witchy, wonderful, we gnash at the world. A poor echo perhaps, but that sound – in a simple way – always recalls for me the thrilling *Laugh of Medusa*. In her text of the same name, Helene Cixous gives Medusa's laugh an expression that is joyously violent, a flood of jouissance. A philosopher of language, Cixous's writing is as vibrant as the laughter she invokes in her essay. And like our delicious kitchen mirth, that laughter opens up a space for female expression.

It is language, Cixous argues, that organises the repressive structure of thinking and narration of experience which has cast women as 'Other' within a phallocentric tradition. A tradition in which woman is posited as 'Other' to man; not in equal opposition, but as an essential alterity through which man understands his own subjectivity. "Since the coming of the patriarchy", Simone de Beauvoir writes in *The Second Sex*, "life in man's eyes has taken on a dual aspect: it is consciousness, will, transcendence, it is intellect and it is matter, passivity, immanence, it is flesh"(p169). These are the essential dualistic myths; sexual myths that align with the asymmetry of male and female. Where man is the Sun, fire, the light of Reason, woman is the Moon, the dark waters of the sea, the carnality of Nature. As the embodiment of reproductive possibility, woman incarnates Nature and thereby personifies both the magic of fertility and the devastation of death. However, while she is given this power, she is not seen to wield it; rather, she is the vessel, the channel, the body through which magic passes. These unconscious yet vital forces must be controlled by Reason and so she, like Nature, is subordinated to man. And because vital transformation occurs through her, when harnessed and exploited, she is "the perfect intermediary between nature that is foreign to man and peer who is too identical to him" (de Beauvoir, p164). As such, woman is the mediator through which man posits himself: "she is… considered not positively, as she is for herself; but negatively, such as she appears to man" (de Beauvoir, p167). "The Laugh of Medusa" is the antithesis of this myth: it is the release, the expression, the roaring insistence of the female as subject.

Across her theoretical writings, Cixous considers this 'othering' of women via the gender binary as represented and compounded by literary texts, classic theatre, myth and legend, allusion and metaphor – found throughout culture from fairy tales to James Joyce's *Ulysses* to the story of Medusa. From within this deep 'cultural mud' women of all kinds must somehow negotiate their subjectivity. Medusa's laugh appears as a kind of catalyst, a Big Bang moment of energetic release; a forceful dispersal of all this heavy material, opening up new dimensions in which to project, to stretch ourselves, reviving us with the energy with which to dance. To sing ourselves awake from dreams that are not our own. To reform language itself. To create the "virile myth[s] that would reflect [our] projects" as subjects (de Beauvoir, p167). To this end, Cixous compels women to write themselves: to express their unsung histories, varied sexualities and experiences. More than this, to write a new kind of writing, an exploded discourse of knowledge and understanding: an Écriture féminine. It is the act of writing itself that unleashes Medusa's riotous gaiety: a writing that expresses her transgressive and transformative laugh and can "smash everything… shatter the framework of institutions… blow up the law… break up the 'truth' with laughter" (Cixous, p888).

Far more often, however, Medusa is simply screaming, her ugly face a torturous death mask. We are far more familiar with a defeated, disembowelled and dismembered monster than this gleefully disruptive vision. Cixous no doubt chose Medusa as her laughing agent in order to subvert the classical myth, one that essentially functions as a deadly warning against the radical dangers of female agency. As acclaimed classical historian Mary Beard shrewdly comments, "It doesn't need Freud to see those snakey locks as an implied claim to phallic power" (p10). A symbol, we must note, that is still very much in use today. Beard clearly illustrates this in her recent article *Women in Power*, using contemporary female politicians such as Theresa May, Angela Merkel and most recently (perhaps most brutally), Hilary Clinton as examples. All have been painted, quite literally, as the archetypal female monster to be defied, defeated and grossly ridiculed. Medusa's story, her beheading at the hands of the hero Perseus "remains even now a cultural symbol of opposition to women's power" (Beard, p12). Medusa as a monster persists as a decapitated figurehead, the repulsion of and to female power. (See Cellini's sixteenth-century bronze statue, the artwork adapted to bear the faces of Donald Trump and Hilary Clinton.)

Like Cixous, de Beauvoir wades through the cultural mud in an attempt to unearth the basic elements of the essentialist myths of womanhood that could inspire such hatred. She calls on our terrible goddesses: Kali, Ishtar, Astarte, Cybele, queens of death as well as bringers of life. Man's supposed destiny means nothing to these lustful creatures; their benevolence is arbitrary. They are fearsome, magnificent, capricious and sometimes cruel, as is "murderous Nature".

Born of woman, man is thus "chained to flesh" (de Beauvoir, p169). His mind, his reason, desperately pulls from the bondage of the body – but in desiring women he is returned once more to weak, dying flesh. Envisioning himself capable of becoming god-like, he is finally reduced by nature, limited by an unfeeling, indifferent mother: "Mother Earth has a face of darkness: she is chaos... she is Nothingness" (de Beauvoir, p170). However, if "Nature is originally bad" it is "powerless when countered with Grace". The good woman, the good mother, the good wife, "loses none of her primitive attributes, but their meanings change; from calamitous they become auspicious; black magic turns to white magic"(de Beauvoir, p195). Her power is directed to the good and, surrounded by priests and men of authority and made dependent on the husband, she is ceremonially purified of her more "disquieting virtues" (de Beauvoir, p192). Beckoning heavenwards, the new eternal feminine takes the form of the Virgin Mary: the idol of birth without sin, life without death.

Solidly settled in the family and society, in accord with laws and customs, the mother is the very incarnation of the Good: the nature in which she participates becomes Good; she is no longer the spirit's enemy; and although she remains mysterious, it is a smiling mystery, like Leonardo da Vinci's Madonna
(de Beauvoir, p195).

Sanctified and servile, the eternal mythic feminine is abstracted as an inanimate ideal. She is Liberty, Wisdom, Chastity. She is the mountain to be conquered, the ocean to be crossed, the night, the cyclical moon. She carries man as his craft; she is the ship, the great machine, forged and cast by him. She is the city that shelters and elevates him to the heavens of his ambition. De Beauvoir writes: "Man feminises the ideal he posits before him as the essential Other, because woman is the tangible figure of alterity" (p202). With her secret smile she can validate man and all of his works. Yet, lurking beneath the surface, perhaps behind that mysterious smile, there remains an eternal horror. Our Medusa. The female monster. The bad mother. The vamp. The flipside of female fertility – beauty and desire – is always decay and death: "the great reaper is the inverted figure of corn-growing fertility. But it is also the frightening wife whose skeleton appears under deceitful and tender flesh" (de Beauvoir, p188). Embodying nature, whether mother or spouse, she is habitually characterised as two-faced and duplicitous. As the conduit of life, woman offers transcendence but also promises death. She gives everything and nothing all at once. In woman we find an endless capacity for corruption.

Delilah and Judith, Aspasia and Lucretia, Pandora and Athena, woman is both Eve and the Virgin Mary. She is an idol, a servant, a source of life, power of darkness; she is the elementary silence of truth, she is artifice, gossip and lies; she is the medicine woman and the witch; she is man's prey; she is his downfall, she is everything he is not and wants to have, his negation and raison d'etre (de Beauvoir, p166).

Essentialised by her carnal biology, her sexual desires and the enjoyment of her powers become particularly abject, as is the desire she kindles in others: "Eve is given to Adam for him to accomplish his transcendence in her and she draws him into the night of immanence" (de Beauvoir, p187). The anxious male gaze renders her beast-like, a primal singularity, an idea, rather than a flesh and blood woman and his very likeness. In deviation from the rules of society that bind her prowess, she once again aligns with

Little Red Cap I (Natalie Frank, 2011)
Gouache and chalk pastel on Arches paper.
Reproduced with kind permission from Natalie Frank • natalie-frank.com •

Little Red Cap II (Natalie Frank, 2011)
Gouache and chalk pastel on Arches paper.
Reproduced with kind permission from Natalie Frank • natalie-frank.com •

Little Red Cap III (Natalie Frank, 2011)
Gouache and chalk pastel on Arches paper.
Reproduced with kind permission from Natalie Frank • natalie-frank.com •

chaotic nature and the devil, exposing the group to evil. The monster must be slain: "All of the idols invented by man, however terrifying he may have made them, are in fact dependent on him, and this is why he is able to destroy them" (de Beauvoir, p84). We return to the supposed vanity of Medusa, her punishment for competing with the goddess Athena, a construction of non-femininity borne literally from the head of the patriarch and to whom the murdered Medusa's head is given as a symbol of her pre-eminence as the logo-centric daughter of patriarchy.

In some cases, our quelled female monster takes on the softer if no less poisonous persona of the fallen woman: the regretful penitent, mournful in her shame but still beautiful and still desirable. This, of course, is how I first drew Medusa, aged 17, in charcoal and pencil. Taking the face of a model from a magazine, who turned her handsome, sculpted face to the camera with an expression of wary submission, mouth puckered and down turned, I coiled her hair into a turban of sinful snakes. "It was her tragedy", I copied below, "that she was foolish enough to compare herself to a goddess." Clearly, I hadn't heard her laugh then. However (and to my present relief), within a few pages of my schoolish scribblings, a different kind of face emerges: that of a Libyan goddess of death and rebirth. I began to draw out her smile, cavernously wide with a fat and fleshy tongue extended in challenge, eyes exaggeratedly bulging from her open, delighted face. This, perhaps, was our brutalised gorgon's potential inspiration: the face of female power that struck an existential fear into the hearts of men. The face that was denied, her sharp-toothed grin masked by the dutiful, self-depreciating smile of the fearful, subjugated female.

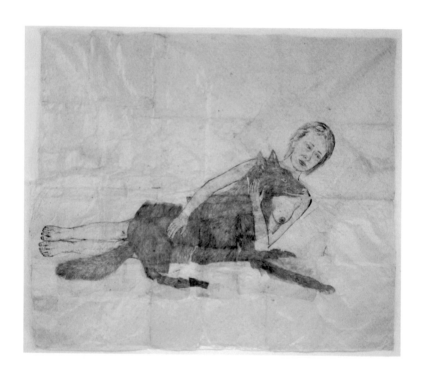

Lying with the Wolf (Kiki Smith, 2001).
Ink and pencil on paper.
Photographed by Ellen Page Wilson.
Reproduced with kind permission from the artist and Pace Gallery, New York.

Rather than a vain woman punished for her pride, the sins attributed more often than not to women, Cixous's laughing Medusa appears to recall the power of this Neolithic snake/bird goddess, creator and destroyer, before she was written into a different story. But of course, there isn't just one story, there are thousands. And even our original myth, the Goddess Mother, "powerful as she may appear... is defined through notions created by the male consciousness" (de Beauvoir, p84). Layer upon layer of myth, retold with multiple agendas, consistently affirm what de Beauvoir calls the "static myth" that divides humanity into two gendered categories; the myths that cast woman as Other so that man may "realise himself thereby as the essential in this alienation he grants" (p275). And unlike our ravaged Medusa, these myths are hard to kill.

The Girl, the Wolf, the Hunger and the Hunt

In examining how subjectivity is understood within a patriarchal tradition of thought as articulated by the creation of the Other, Cixous argues that the formation of dual and hierarchical sexual difference creates a dangerous dialectic of power and inequality; one that has become insidious as that which proposes to underpin desire. A desire that, according to Cixous, only offers women a "choice between castration and decapitation; between internalisation of a structure of desire based on loss, or deadly violence" (Shiach, p8). As the novelist Angela Carter writes:

> To be the object of desire is to be defined in the passive case. To exist in the passive case is to die in the passive case — that is, to be killed (Simpson, 2006).

Monstrous goddess or holy servant, woman is held in the balance between an ideal and its opposition, constantly journeying the path from good to bad, bad to good, and always at risk. In her collection of short stories, *The Bloody Chamber*, Angela Carter takes inspiration from ancient fairytales but diverts from their well-known narratives to allow her female characters to stray from their archetypal roles. These are women full of desire; women with a thirst for experience and freedom who refuse their assigned endings. Here perhaps we might find some semblance of women's dark, dangerous dreams of themselves: the "virile myths" that Cixous urges women to write from an exploded canon of inherited knowledge. The heavy, faded pages of fable start to brighten under Medusa's hungry gaze and from the depths of the dark woods a sudden peal of capricious, girlish laughter takes a big bad wolf by surprise.

Following the trail of *Little Red Riding Hood*, the plot of Carter's short story *The Company of Wolves* unexpectedly twists in the last few hundred words when an unnamed girl sheds her quintessential blood red cape, her clothes and her fear to stand naked and gleaming in the firelight, laughing full into the face of a so-called wolf. Her joyous abandon recalls Medusa's laugh, destabilising the accepted relationship between the hunted and the hunter, and rewriting the apocryphal tale in her own hand. Her grandmother's bones can rattle all they like; "She knew she was nobody's meat" (Carter, 2004). She roars; the wolf licks his chops. And so the girl strips the wolf of his clothes, and savagely grooms and tenderises him in her grandmother's bed.

This Red Riding Hood-inspired section of Carter's story follows a longer introduction that tells a series of cautionary tales featuring the male werewolf, stories that prime the young girl for her relationships with men. This serves as an apt reminder that "for woman it is man who is sexed and carnal" but also of the given female role of sexual prey. While stalling her would-be attacker, a wolf in lice-ridden man-skin, the girl fearfully observes the pack pacing in the snow outside the cottage and recollects her grandmother's warning that "the worst wolves are hairy on the inside". However, we could also read this as a caution against the strength of her own desires. As Cixous asks in *The Laugh of Medusa*,

Who, surprised and horrified by the fantastic tumult of her drives (for she was made to believe that a well-adjusted normal woman has a ... divine composure), hasn't accused herself of being a monster? (p876)

In the end, the wolf is fully revealed, as is the girl sleeping peacefully between its paws. Outside the restful cottage is "snowlight, moonlight" and "a confusion of paw prints" (Carter, 2004). Medusa's joyful battle cry awakens the beast within the girl as much as it exposes the cocky wolf's vulnerability. But it is worth noting that this exchange is still characterised by opposition and conflict; and not only is it a confrontation that presents a deeply unequal risk, but a residual threat remains ever present for the girl navigating the dense, dark forest, even as she refuses her sacrificial status; even as her sweet, pacifying smile breaks into a pointed, hungry grin.

This confusion between beast and man, man and woman, wolf and girl, and the unequal duality of human sexuality can also be found in painter Natalie Frank's revision of the time-worn story. In brilliantly acidic gouache and chalk pastel, Frank renders the tale in a series of three. In the first image, a plump and child-like Little Red Riding Hood stands awkwardly with her back to the viewer before the brazen and devilish wolf, who revels in the bed of the old woman he has just eaten, balls out. Behind the toothy wolf, Red's distressed and contrastingly adult-looking face is reflected back to us in the mirror. We confront the monstrous wolf with her.

The second drawing is a ferocious tangle of limbs – limbs that extend from the wolf-body's every orifice. This scene is captured, according to Frank's accompanying text, at the point at which the heroic huntsman cuts the predatory wolf open to find the two women, one young and one old, improbably intact within. Apparently swallowed whole, the white, foetal granny figure curls up in the belly of the wolf, who appears to blaze with live-wire orange hair sprouting from muscular leg, nipples and a ravening head with its grossly lolling, pastel-blue eye. Red's torso is bent strangely backwards, birthed from between the reclined wolf's legs, her face pale, set and staring. But now one of the wolf's legs is undeniably red, more delicate, and a furry pelt trails, discarded, from its pointed, clawed foot. Above, an incongruently naturalistic human hand reaches out through the wolf's gummy maw. Violently combined, the body of the wolf appears to both consume and produce his prey.

In the final image the wolf is defeated, bound with a belly full of stones. Frank writes:

Little Red Cap fills up the wolf with stones and looks at him face to face. She has been inside him and now faces him, cheek to cheek. Their faces meld together and the picture falls away to abstraction (Reilly, p433).

Different forms of masculinity and femininity collide here; in some cases arrogantly well-formed and made in stark comparison, elsewhere remaining fuzzy and confused. The conclusion of the girl and the wolf's confrontation remains ambiguous. However, the body of the wolf remains the most visually assertive, the most forceful in all three images, posed in contrast with Red's splotchy pinks and crimson patches. Both are perpetually haunted by the ineffectual, pale-pastel grandmother figure who reappears as an angel in the top section of the final image, opposite the smug flourish of the huntsman and diametric to the raised head of a faithful and servile dog in the bottom corner. Bold and bristling with unresolved energy, the wolf and the woman merge in the centre ground. Through her encounter with the wolf, with carnality, the girl appears to have gained something: some self-knowledge perhaps, posed among the hierarchy of pale caricatures that surround them. Within their conflict, there is reciprocity; the predator-prey relationship becomes less distinct as she and the wolf regard one another candidly, her face merging with his. The body becomes a potential site of transformation, as well as entrapment.

The mutuality of the woman and the wolf can also be found in another artist's take on the Little Red Riding Hood theme. Like Frank, Kiki Smith explores the hierarchical relationships at play within the character dynamics of folk tales, reworking the predator-prey relationship between wolf and woman. They find shared comfort in *Lying with the Wolf* (2001), a large-scale pencil and ink drawing on paper that depicts a naked woman clutching the wolf to her, or reaching out to the animal companionably in the bronze *Genevieve and the May Wolf*. Alternately, in *Rapture*

(2001), a woman calmly steps out from the fractured belly of a recumbent wolf in a violent re-birth. In the meeting of these seemingly opposing bodies, the possibility of both cataclysm and connection is suggested with either leading to a form of revelation or transformation quite apart from the original mythic metaphor. Mirroring Smith's *Rapture* is Carter's *The Tiger's Bride* in which, against all odds, a woman retains her sense of self-possession despite being made a captive, bartered and sold by men. Still defiant, but now curious and desiring of new pleasures, the young bride discovers her own striped fur, her luxurious claws, her freedom, as her human skin is lovingly and roughly licked from her by the beast. Tigers, wolves, monsters and lovers prowl between the pages of Carter's collection, but their hunt never ends as expected. As in Frank and Smith's work, old familiar narratives fracture and combine, diverging into new story lines. Women discover their own bodies, their own selves, not as meat to feed the other but as a site of exaltation and expansion. Crucially, the distinctions between gender hierarchy, animalism and humanity, the powerful and the powerless are continually confused, and in that chaos – a chaos that rings with Medusa's rambunctious gaiety – is a kind of clarity.

A clarity that the real relation between subjects is that of reciprocity, retaining both difference and familiarity. The "mystery of the Other is 'reciprocal'", de Beauvoir argues, requiring "the recognition of freedoms that confirm each other" (p278). On the other hand, to posit woman as "the absolute Other, without reciprocity" is to consign her to remaining a "mystery in herself" and to refuse "against experience, that she could be a subject, a peer" (p275). She is distance, unknowable and unknowing. In *Women in Power*, Mary Beard points out that "you can't easily fit women into a structure that is already coded as male; you have to change the structure" (p14). She underscores how we describe the act of female access to the centres of power and influence, with a language that emphasises our exteriority – whether we are politely "knocking on the door", or, understandably fed up of waiting to be let in, violently "storming the citadel" and gleefully "smashing the glass ceiling" (p9). In fact, the violence of these latter expressions only exemplifies how female claims to power, space, pleasure and to our own bodies, to our anger at being denied these things, are frequently cast as dangerous, nonsensical demands, immune to order and peace. Here there be monsters.

Such a dialectic turns the erotic object into female black magic, turns the female servant into a traitor, Cinderella into a witch, and changes all woman into the enemy: here is the ransom man pays for having posited himself in bad faith as sole essential (de Beauvoir, p214).

Designated as "the carnal embodiment of all moral values and their opposites" woman becomes "the source of all man's reflection on his existence" and so "as his servant and companion, man also expects her to be his public and his judge, to confirm him in his being" (de Beauvoir , p219). But what if she does not smile upon him? What if she doesn't recognise her Prince Charming as the one who awakens her? Might she oppose him, be indifferent to him, laugh at and mock him? Her freedom always comes at his expense, although she only belittles him to the extent that she renders him as finite and earthly as herself. To insist on a negative relationship, rather than one of reciprocity, is to remain trapped in a constant struggle.

The world's true meaning is found at the level of communication...To say that woman is a mystery is not to say that she is silent but that her language is not heard (de Beauvoir, p278).

The Art of the Female Monster

In a 2015 interview published as an introduction to her anthology of essays *Women Artists*, the eminent art critic Linda Nochlin comments that "As a feminist, I fear this moment's overt reversion to the most blatant forms of patriarchy, a great moment for so-called 'real men' to assert their sinister dominance over 'others'" (Reilly, p40). In *Why Have There Been No Great Women Artists? Thirty Years After*, a 2006 response to her famous 1971 essay, Nochlin stresses the continued need to insist upon the visibility of women and the expression of their varied experience: "We need all our wit and courage to make sure that women's voices are heard, their work seen and written about. That is our task for the future" (Reilly, p320).

As Mary Beard recently underlined in *Women in Power*, we know that taking up space and speaking out is a powerfully transgressive act for any woman, and so much more for some than others; as is any expressive act that brings her and her body into a space where it is not welcome, where it doesn't behave as it should, where it is not recognised as legitimate, where it becomes too large and too loud and thereby becomes grotesque, profane, and is labelled 'monstrous'. And what if that monstrous body were to laugh?

In this respect it is critical that Cixous's mouthy mutiny in language is an embodied expression. Not only within the easy proximity of the voice to writing, but in her focus on the monstrous female body and the bodily female monster; our Medusa shaking with laughter, with delight, with rage. Laughter is the release point for Cixous's Écriture féminine; laughter that sings through the body. This initially seems like a dangerous mistake: to situate her where she has been most assailable. Indeed, that the female body itself, the writing female body, is at the core of Cixous's text, has been carefully critiqued many times in feminist thought as risking a reductive essentialism, or biological determinacy of femaleness that reproduces the very structures of oppression she would seem to wish to destroy. In a "writing of the body", as theorist Morag Shiach explains, "we fear appropriation at the point where we have been, historically, most vulnerable, and where we have been so ruthlessly placed" (p20).

Yet, "to evade the bodily is [also] to reproduce a structure of oppression which has made women's bodies their point of vulnerability and guilt" (Shiach, p20). As described above, the 'othering' of woman in a patriarchal tradition means that her body is not understood as an emanation of her subjectivity but as a "thing weighted in its immanence". The only power woman has is as a natural object: a body that "must not radiate to the rest of the world… must not promise anything but itself: its desire must be stopped" (de Beauvoir, p181). However, in Carter's short stories, in Frank and Smith's work, in their rewriting of myth and legend, we find the female subject emerging from the body, from women's desires and from their encounters with the other, even from the contradictions and dangers therein. The body becomes a space in which to assert their humanity and, in doing so, to expressly distance femininity from the more marvellous qualities of the mythic eternal feminine. In fact, the expression of female subjectivity through an art form that brings a non-idealised female body into the purity of the gallery space is a doubly sharp challenge to the idea that woman is "not subject, transcendence, or creative power, but an object charged with fluids" (de Beauvoir, p287). Kiki Smith even turns these fluids into jewels, such as in *Pee Body* (1992) in which a female figure squats to release a gush of yellow beads, or the standing female form of *Untitled* (Train, 1993), who calmly observes the trail of blood-red beads she has left behind her. Where the classical body of traditional sculpture avoids its material reality, Smith smears the white cube with the evidence for it. As Nochlin writes, "There is something scary and taboo about incorporating the bodily functions that Smith engages with so boldly into the work of art, as though revealing them suggests that the body itself is only a work in progress, as it were; ephemeral, debased, mortal" (Reilly, p299).

Writing 'through the body' as Cixous desires is to understand ourselves as bodies that are culturally inscribed rather than 'natural'. The body is represented, coded, constructed of a language that we inhabit and re-present. Of course, the dilemma is as real and physical as it is theoretical, as it is written, as it is lived. Through her proposed Écriture féminine, Cixous looks to a way in which we might reform the language we have been given to express our subjectivities with and experience a more spacious skin.

If woman has always functioned "within" the discourse of man, a signifier that has always referred back to the opposite signifier which annihilates its specific energy and diminishes or stifles its

very different sounds, it is time for her to dislocate this "within", to
explode it, turn it around, and seize it; to make it hers, containing
it, taking it in her own mouth, biting that tongue with her very
own teeth to invent for herself a language
to get inside of (Cixous, p887).

In order to posit ourselves, we must take a stand where we have been "so ruthlessly placed", as Shiach put it: "one cannot simply walk out of patriarchy and shake off its effects" (p20). There may, in fact, be very little choice in the matter. We are descendants of Eve, not Lilith, who unlike her younger sister was made of the same primeval dust as Adam and, refusing her proposed subjugation to him, defiantly departed the Earth for the stars beyond. Perhaps we will encounter her someday. In the meantime, we must take control of the codes that have written us. Twist the tongues we have been given into our own shapes and sounds. As Linda Nochlin succinctly put it in her 1976 essay, *Women Artists After the French Revolution*:

...to discard obviously mystificatory, essentialist theories about
women's "natural" directions in art is by no means to affirm that
the fact of being a woman is completely irrelevant
to artistic creation (p115).

In fact, to abscond from that position is to leave women's contradictory existence unchallenged. In writing, "painting [her] half of the world" and singing "unknown songs" she may usefully trouble the culture that has made woman a mystery to herself (Cixous, p876). To challenge an ideal is always to risk appearing monstrous, but Cixous urges us to persist, even from a compromised position. Here I can't help but think of Chris Kraus's love letter entitled "Monster": a chapter of her book of letters *I Love Dick* in which she discusses the failure of the art world audience to really see Hannah Wilke, at least within the artist's lifetime; instead looking away from beauty and then from narcissism, and never quite seeing the incomparable work itself. Risking herself, her body, her female personhood as material for her artwork, Wilke continually divided opinion, whether coveted as a symbol of sexual liberation or denied as narcissistic and dangerous self-display, with few feeling beyond their own embarrassment: "as if the point were not the revealing of the circumstances of one's own objectification. As if Hannah Wilke was not brilliantly feeding back the audience's prejudices and fear, inviting them to join her for a naked lunch."

For Kraus, Wilke is the aspirational model of the female monster, forceful in her fragility. "Female monsters", she explains, in comparison to the confident vanity of the male genius, "take things as personally as they really are." And they are uncompromising in their relentless will to expose themselves and the conditions of their selfhood. To understand why they are shameful.

Monstrosity: the self as machine. The Blob, mindlessly swallowing and engorging, rolling down the supermarket aisle absorbing pancake mix and jello and everyone in town. Unwise and unstoppable. The horror of The Blob is the horror of the fearless. To become The Blob requires a certain force of will (Kraus).

That will, that brilliant and dauntless challenge, is the essence of Cixous's *Laugh of Medusa* and that which continues to enrapture me, perhaps due to the fact that its trappings are so obviously and essentially present, embraced even. The image of the laughing Medusa is appealing due to her obvious lack of fear despite being named a monster.

She laughs perhaps because her monstrosity is a given and is to be revealed and revelled in; that in writing the female body, in interleaving physical and intellectual jouissance, in expressing an undefined, expansive sexuality at its core, she will be read as monstrous.

Yet she laughs, and it's a very freeing thought.

You only have to look at the Medusa straight on to see her. And she's not deadly. She's beautiful and she's laughing (Cixous, p885).

And laughter is infectious. With Wilke as her model, Kraus declares that she too "aims to be a female monster". I believe we must experience our own "admirable hysterics", the voices of women that Nochlin writes must be elevated and projected, and I take note whenever I find I can hear Medusa's distinct, dark humour. Indeed, I experienced her powerful mirth on a recent visit to Gazelli Art House, London, where I was elated to see two of Nancy's Spero's energetic Dildo Dancers. The dancing figures in Spero's prints are a distilled version of the classical vase designs of Ancient Greece: solid, flat, bold negations of space and colour. But, breaking the mould somewhat, these vital, monstrous dancers leap enthusiastically with an enormous dildo in each hand. Their glee is, as Spero has commented, either "murderous or joyous". Deathly white, the gallery suddenly succumbed to Medusa's laughter. Seeing, hearing, feeling her brutal laughter is so much more than cathartic. It inspires others to show their teeth. It is laughter that swells the body, crashes through it, bursts out into the world. Laughter that consumes shame, burns with it, defies it, so that laughing bodies ripple with delightful vitriol. Lit up. Let it burn. Yes, sometimes it is a great anger that gives energy to this movement. On that particular day, I also visited Tyburn Gallery and found the walls were aflame with *Lust Politics*, an exhibition of work by South African artist Lady Skollie. Like Wilke, Lady Skollie isn't "afraid to call a cunt a cunt" (or a dick a dick, I would presume), repeating the motif in her *Pussy Print* series. Nor is she afraid to "throw back to the audience everything the world throws at me" (Kraus). For Lady Skollie, art is necessarily a confrontation with that which makes us uncomfortable, that which makes us angry. Apples, bananas, papayas and pussies are simultaneously richly erotic and vulnerable to ugly consumption. Their comically blatant objectiveness is confronted with the violence and oppressive power structures that abuses and confines the body and its erotic joy. The wiggling pink worms amongst a cascade of yellow bananas is entitled *Pink Dick: Sometimes I reluctantly reflect on all the times I allowed my pussy to be colonized*. Rage seeps through the garish humour: "I am so angry and I don't know how to tell you without smashing things. I am so angry."

Lady Skollie's fervent desire for "everything to burn so that we can start again" taps into the expelled frustration of Medusa's laugh. Much of Cixous's scholarly position involves an in-depth deconstruction of the origins of patriarchy and its hierarchies of power in literature, philosophy and myth, and works through her awareness of her own embeddedness in that discourse. An Écriture féminine, like Medusa's laugh, offers some relief, some further strategy: "What I say has at least two sides and two aims: to break up, to destroy, and to foresee the unforeseeable, to project" (Cixous, p875). In some cases, laughter can change the tone of the conversation. Medusa's laugh obliterates it. Diverting and divisive, it is enticingly suggestive of a potential game changer.

Most importantly, within Medusa's unapologetic and devastating wake, amongst the loosened, unfastened concepts, there is variety and multiplicity. Subjects do not define themselves by refusal or appropriation of the Other but create an expansive place of "exchange in which each one would keep the Other alive and different". At least, this is what Cixous conjures as an Écriture féminine: an "infinite richness", an "inexhaustible imaginary" (p876). The female subject as a prodigious many.

In concrete reality, women manifest themselves in many different ways, but each of the myths built around women tries to summarise her as a whole (de Beauvoir, p275).

As Nochlin argues, there is no evidence of a feminine style and therefore, women's art – their expression – must always be understood as plural. One could go further and say that any ideal of female visibility remains a fallacy if it is not understood as varied and variable. If the mystery of the other and their shared nature is not respected for all subjects. To write as such, within, without and with desire, remains a tantalising challenge. To write oneself from within one space to a place beyond, and all the while to keep the 'Other' alive and different is a goal to be ever reached for. And Medusa's laugh carries and is always an invitation to join her. As Wilke proffered, you need to "become your own myth". So, like Kraus, I aim to be a voluminous female monster, "a frivolous female, a femme-fatale with evil intention, a neo-hysteric, an erotic with a problem" (Foad, et al), unapologetically embarrassing, forceful, fragile, truthful and raw, smiling with sharp teeth sheathed in desiring flesh.

Hairy on the inside.

Womanhood

Brook Shelley

Defining womanhood reminds me of the adage about the fish trying to understand water. How can we understand ourselves as women, as experiencing womanhood except through contrast? If we have experiences that are outside of the typical frame of white cisgender femininity, does that make us less of a woman, or expand what woman means? I strongly believe the latter is true but from the myriad books and articles on womanhood, you'd think it was the former. Let's do that thing where we look at a dictionary:

a : the state of being a woman

b : the distinguishing character or qualities of a woman or of womankind

With womanhood describing the state of being a woman, we don't get very far before we have to return, again, to the tome of words:

a : an adult female person

b : a woman belonging to a particular category

And with the definition of woman, we get to the animal descriptor of 'female', which really, at its crux reduces us to our ability to potentially birth young, and other qualities that don't make for a very progressive lens of more than half of the human race. And so, womanhood still feels precariously defined. Are we really the sum of our biology? Where does this leave women without wombs? Women who experience miscarriages, or choose not to have children? Those of us with intermittent cycles, or no cycle? Even among cis women, there are so many variations and varieties of body and experience that attempting to single-out a 'female' experience or body is a futile task. But clearly, the category of woman, and the idea of womanhood, is still something that both exists and affects all of us daily.

In a time where women still make less than men, are at higher risk of violence, lack of healthcare and so many other terrible things, being a woman is not exactly enviable. And, as many folks have discovered the plasticity of gender and a hoped for liminal space without or between genders, those that claim womanhood have changed as well. Semantics won't save us from the world, but they do help organise it – and us – and in that unity perhaps we can find change? The history of women's rights, though disturbingly slow to include new women outside the affluent white, landed gentry, is one of advocating for women being more than mothers, house-labourers, or wives. Yet, when we reach to define and understand womanhood, it seems we so often lean on these old tropes.

So, how do you know you're a woman? What does womanhood feel like? To me it feels like having a body. Womanhood is something I don't notice unless it's blemished, or hurt by outside forces. I experience the world through it but am also contained by it. It took me a while to find my way to womanhood, but less because I'm trans and more because the definitions and descriptions of womanhood I grew up around implied heterosexuality, passivity and a proclivity for pink. I'm a tomboyish dyke. The idea of woman as a person who marries a man, raises children and vacuums constantly had no appeal – and like modern women, I felt hemmed in and uncomfortable. I carved out a space for myself, while usually seen by the world as a man, to explore what I could of womanhood. I tried to understand what womanhood could be and not just what it so often was. I read other women who fought for an expansion of our definition. I spent time with girls and women who played loud, brash punk music; women who slept with each other and spit, and rode bicycles angrily through the night. I watched some of the tough women change and shift as they got older, married, had children. For some of us, it seemed that our fight for new avenues of womanhood was time-bound by our youth. It is so easy to give in and follow the script we've read since birth. But many of us keep fighting, even from positions that may appear staid.

Perhaps it's useful to determine what kind of woman I am before we move forward. At present I'm a woman on a couch in Portland, Oregon. I'm heavily tattooed, pantsless, and drinking coffee. I'm equipped with four limbs, 10 toes and fingers, and hair that is longer in the front than the back. I wear glasses. My ears are pierced, as is my nose. I'm white and earn a yearly salary. I deal with depression and trauma. My birth certificate probably still says 'M', but nothing else that describes me does. I grew up in Texas, but you wouldn't hear it in my voice were I reading this to you out loud. I travel often, and am attracted to other women, and sometimes people who aren't women but aren't men either. The venn diagram of what 'woman' includes overlaps me quite a bit, but as many women who slightly diverge from this all-encompassing womanhood have found, the parts outside the circle are where the trouble lies.

As a dyke, the history of our exclusion from womanhood is a trouble I'm intimately familiar with since first reading about Betty Friedan coining the phrase 'Lavender Menace' to describe the lesbian activists being pushed out of the women's rights movement. The heterocentrist women's rights movement had included lesbians since its beginning with suffragists in England and America, but as it tried to better assimilate with mainstream society, the exclusion of those that transgressed societal standards continued.

The roots of suffrage and other women's rights movements similarly excluded women of colour, trans women, otherly-abled women and many other varieties of woman. Because of this exclusion, and the intentionality behind it, history books and school curriculum convince many of us that our womanhood isn't valid. We don't see each other represented in pictures, words, or song. This exclusion from a common women's narrative means that many of us are forced to construct and understand our womanhood as outsiders, or with qualifiers. 'Trans womanhood' or 'Black womanhood', which both serve to indicate difference from the position of a bog standard womanhood. But, the problem I fear, goes much deeper. Even the exclusive womanhood of the white, thin and cis is built in opposition to the human narrative of man. Men, we're told, are tough, strong and capable. Women are the 'other half' cleft from Adam's rib. We're the soft to man's rough. Books that have a female protagonist are called out for being women's literature and are presumed to tell a narrower and more specific story than one with a man at the helm.

I'd hope that if you're reading this, you know better. You know that there is no singular womanhood to oppose a singular manhood. That womanhood doesn't imply an other, because there's no 'there' to gender. Gender is both constructed and relational, and so the ways we build ours and the gender around us are in constant flux as we discuss and live with each other. 'Woman' can be a political rallying cry, or something to abandon as we seek other words. Though, in our haste to make new things, I fear we sometimes define ourselves as 'not-woman', instead of in some other more positive way. I'm not sure what the responsibility of genderqueer, agender, or non-binary folks is towards womanhood, or the women who either feel at home in some version of womanhood, or haven't yet learned there's new vistas to explore. It's more than understandable that for many folks, the yolk of a heterocentrist definition fits poorly, but between an antagonist birth assignment of 'sex' and the reality of misogyny that relishes destroying our identities lies a world of questions. If we truly want to destroy binaries, to build up a more expansive world of gender, we can't do so alone; we must include and fight for heterosexual, cisgender women even as we try to obviate those very concepts.

To return to semantics, I don't think new words can liberate or save a category of people that is multivalent but generally worse-off than the men of our species. But I do think it's useful to define ourselves how we like. For many of us, this feels like we're party to a war we didn't start and would prefer to avoid — a battle of the sexes that would rather have us for fodder than listen to the words we speak to challenge and obviate the entire struggle. A battle that regulates and controls our bodies, whether or not we consider them 'women's bodies'. Because, at the end of the day, the ways we construct our identities and our internal sense of self still may be opposed to the material reality of the countries we inhabit. There's the world we dream of and the one we live in, and in both places we situate ourselves in relation to womanhood.

Let's explore the body further. When you read 'a woman's body' – what do you think? Is the body curvy? Is it brown? How closely does it resemble your own? What parts and shapes are a prerequisite for your concept, regardless of how your politics correct your initial image? Is it a body you desire to inhabit, sleep with, or both? Can you feel the edges of your self, the body that you are a part of? How do you contrast and compare this body with 'a woman's body'? Really think about it, even if you have pat answers you're quick to provide, because while many of us have considered our body – are raised to judge ourselves against an ideal of women's bodies – few of us interrogate our bodies with an open and loving heart. To me, a woman's body is inclusive of my own, but expansive as well. All shapes, configurations, races and expressions can have a home under these words. And while I'm sure there are many folks who cringe at the idea of 'women's body'– it's very important to understand why. In the aforementioned war against women's bodies, many of us are unknowingly complicit; buying whole-cloth the notion that women's bodies are lesser, are weak, are impossible to achieve. It's certainly great to have or not have a woman's body, but even in my own life, I built it as a bogeywoman for too long and then realised my idealised body already existed in the thought – 'I'm enough.' Like many women, I internalised a vast world of standards for myself and the concept of 'woman'. I thought I knew I couldn't transition because I'd never pass, or I was too muscular, or my face had certain angles. One day, I no longer thought that, or was at least able to take the chance that it didn't matter and the patriarchy was perhaps poisoning me against myself. It was worth it to interrogate and move past those feelings and find a new internal standard for myself built on love and self-acceptance. When we hold each other's bodies up as yardsticks for what gender looks like, what womanhood looks like, all of us fail to measure up. What would it look like if instead, we recognise the fractal, multifaceted reality of womanhood and the body therein. How would that shift our discourse? How would accepting ourselves, if we are women or if we are not, change the way we speak and perform our work?

And how does desire work, inside womanhood? It's common, I think, for desire to be characterised by the other. But isn't a woman's desire often encompassed in our own identity, our own personhood? This isn't the bad joke about lesbians being so self-obsessed that we date other women but something more subtle. This idea of looking for like, of looking for the very womanhood that we claim, to validate it, to explore it, to touch another part of ourselves. There are mirrors and there are relationships, and both reflect more about us than we might be comfortable with.

This is further complicated by being an adult woman, desiring other adult women. Too often our desires are demeaned or belittled. We have to be cute, or demure, but I want full industrial grade sapphism. A woman, loving herself as such and loving another woman for all that she is, embodied and strong, is beautiful. But, it's hard to find. A lot has been written about butch and femme dynamics and what that means in some cases for women's desire for masculinity – but femme and butch are both queer expressions of womanhood that are perfectly valid. Masculinity and femininity, both constructed, are not intrinsic parts of womanhood, but can be applied in degrees by a woman at her will. In some cases, the playful counterpoints of short hair with a dress, or long hair and jean cut-offs can reveal the joy of a spectrum of womanhood. And while straight and bisexual women also experiment and play with gender presentation inside of womanhood, the vastness is often limited by proximity to male desire. In a place of women's desire for women, we're free to explore and sometimes codify our new attractions and desires. What does it mean to say a woman is boyish? How does that change or interact with our own womanhood, especially a lesbian womanhood? If we expand womanhood to include women enacting a certain masculine style, or boldly expressing themselves in a mode deemed manly by those with outdated views on gender, I think we better ourselves and our world.

For a thought experiment, think through your past few lovers, or dates. Now, consider if they would say they experience womanhood. What does their womanhood look like? How do they present? What is their style? What combination of sights, sounds, smells, and words from them led to your attraction? How do these dates reflect on each other? Is there variance in your desires, or do you have a strong 'type' that you seek out or are receptive to? If you think very hard for a minute, what might your 'type,' or pattern of dating say about your internalised or externalised racial, class, or physical prejudices or fears? There isn't a right answer but this exercise can be illuminating to our construction of ourselves and others as sexually compatible or interesting. Through this journey, we may find uncomfortable things out about ourselves, but instead of throwing in the towel and hiding behind the common, "I like what I like, what's the problem?" think about the potential problems inherent in consciously or unconsciously limiting ourselves to someone who perhaps most closely approximates a cis and heteronormative beauty – or an impish boyishness or harsh and strong masculinity that makes us feel more complete or needed. What happens to our desires if we learn to love ourselves first? What if we are enough on our own, so completion and need aren't granted primacy in our dating life? It's possible that with self-work and self-love we may learn just how limited our desires were in the past and why our relationships often repeated the same patterns, as we searched for the validation that necessarily comes from within.

My own experiences of other women and non-binary folks' embodiments as my lovers and dates are varied, but often only through intentional work on who and what I find attractive. I too am a woman in this world and do not love myself perfectly, but I gently prod and ask questions of myself each time I find someone attractive: What is it that attracts me to this person? How do these qualities echo the societal lens that I'm a part of? What does queernormative look like?

No one should ever be an experiment but once you expand the definition of desirable you may find, as I have, dating becomes better all around. There are literally more fish in the sea.

Similarly, though my experience with desiring men is extremely limited, I feel that the expansion of manhood is equally important. There's no Venn diagram where manhood and womanhood aren't overlapping, and encouraging those who enjoy or inhabit manhood into feminine and masculine modes and dress makes the daily experience of both men and women better. With this overlap, we can understand more about each other and enjoy the plasticity of gender and expression. Desiring effeminate men does not mean someone is less of a man, or woman. We don't need opposition or stark contrast in every case to engender desire, or find our place in the world. A shifting vista of styles and lives is a noble goal, in this author's opinion.

But, back to womanhood and our internal judge. When we measure ourselves against the construct of womanhood, the 'must be this gender' to ride sign, what is measured? Is it our proximity to a cisgender 'norm'? Our closeness to a mainstream ideal of heterosexual desire? Is it through the eyes of another woman, or a dark and handsome man? Or, do we interrogate ourselves against a varied world of femininity, supplemented by pages of white, thin Cosmopolitan women? I've known women who forever judge themselves against their mothers or grandmothers and others who don't have time between surviving to have these existential crises. So often, those of us striving to put food on the table for ourselves or our families aren't able to afford complicated thoughts about our failure to live up to whatever standards society or ourselves has for women's appearances. Many of us learn to compartmentalise and put away any self-loathing we might pick up in the air for another day. And, for women engaging in sex work, appearances of a particular sort become intrinsically linked to financial circumstance, with some finding freedom in the clarity. But all of us inhabit the same Earth and in each culture and sub-culture there are standards, mores and -isms that influence how we judge and view ourselves – this is to say, none of us is an island. The existence of prejudices and judgments aren't limited to those external to womanhood either, as we often internalise our feelings. Fat women can be internally fatphobic. Trans women internally transphobic and so forth. It's especially because of this that it's so important to learn more about our ways of judging ourselves. Once we situation ourselves and our lens to the world, we're more likely able to interrogate the treatment and desire (or disgust) engendered by others. A wider swathe of identities, presentations, bodies, and life-experiences in our friend groups can cement this idea that womanhood is multivalent and we, as women, are enough. This challenge of a monolithic standard refuses to bend to the covergirl mentality as we learn to see through this ruse.

We began this investigation into womanhood with a dictionary, but I hope that by this point, you know womanhood is so much more. There is no 'womanhood' in the sense that there is no there there. We relate to each other and ourselves in unique and shifting manners, and recognising the huge spectrum of womanhood – and even manhood – expands our own definition, even as it ads new adjectives and descriptors to womanhood itself. Instead of a list of qualifications, we may end up with a virtual smörgåsbord with which to say "I am a woman," or "I experience and feel womanhood." As our understanding of gender grows societally and personally, I hope we don't abandon ideas of woman or manhood completely but instead learn to embrace their qualities for ourselves, regardless of assignment, or gender. Instead of finding a new definition for womanhood, perhaps we've found that womanhood defies definition. Find your place inside or outside of it, but always try to understand and respect those that end up in any relation to it. Truly, womanhood is the summation of everything we are and can be as people.

Authentic(ated) Author –
Writing and (Gender) Identity

James Bradfield and Ever Dundas

I'm James Bradfield.

I'm 85 years old and grew up in London in WWII before travelling with the circus across post-war Europe. My first novel, *Goblin*, is written under the name Ever Dundas. Ever is an actor I hired to be me because I value my privacy. Ever appears at all my events, reading from *Goblin*. She pretends to be a shy introvert who doesn't like answering questions about her life.

No one has questioned her authenticity. No one has questioned whether she can write about WWII London when she hasn't lived in London and didn't experience the war. She says she wrote a female protagonist who is sometimes mistaken for, or pretends to be, a boy because that was her experience growing up.

But now I want to come forward – I am James Bradfield and I wrote *Goblin*.

I wanted someone to hide behind; I didn't want people to intrude on my life. I was concerned people would pick holes in my depiction of a female protagonist. Because *Goblin's* gender identity isn't straightforward, I thought they would say I was imposing male characteristics onto a girl.

This essay was born out of discussions Ever and I had about gender and authorship. Ever studied drama at university, where she read feminism and Queer Theory, and Judith Butler's *Gender Trouble* became her Bible. We decided Ever would write this piece and the final edit would be a collaboration. Let us take you on a journey through authorship, identity and gender.

***

The Grand Narrative of Gender and Gendered Fiction

"What DOES make a character believable as a girl or a boy? Is it simply conformity to our own notions of femininity and masculinity, which are in turn heavily influenced by culture, epoch, and our own personal gender identity? Or are there any fixed measures?" (Sensel, 2009).

This is an extract from a blog on the topic of *Gender and Perception*, which focuses on whether authors can convincingly write protagonists of the 'opposite' sex. By 'fixed measures' I'm assuming the blogger is referring to a prediscursive, essentialist notion of sex/gender, particularly as she already highlights cultural influence. What's interesting here is the suggestion that we could measure a fictional character's gender 'authenticity' by recourse to a prediscursive law. In *Gender Trouble* Judith Butler argues that a prediscursive law reifies the notion of a fixed, foundationalist sex, and that "by telling a single, authoritative account about an irrecoverable past, makes the constitution of the law appear as a historical inevitability" (Butler, 1999).

The blogger goes on to write: "most of us have read adult books by an author writing an MC [main character] of the opposite gender and felt that the author perhaps did not do so authentically (which makes those who do succeed that much more impressive.)" (Sensel, 2009). This raises the question, why is it seen to be such a feat for a man to write a female protagonist or a woman to write a male protagonist?

The *Gender and Perception* blogger followed up with a comment on a character she wasn't convinced by: "I kept looking for a shred of femininity or feminine communication style in the character, and not finding it. I am hardly a girly girl myself, but it was just one of the things that made me not really 'trust' the author" (Sensel, 2009). It's worrying that a reader won't go on a journey with a writer because the characters don't conform to the reader's gender experiences/prejudices. Butler interrogates the grand narrative of gender: the 'truth' and naturalness of the binary opposition 'male/female' is shown to be a construction, performance, "imitation without an origin" (Butler, 1999). Butler exposes gender as a fiction. There's an irony when fiction is expected to reify the fictive categories of gender as prediscursive and fixed.

In a blog post giving advice on *Writing Characters of the Opposite Gender* Mette Ivie Harrison says: "Male and female characters are people before they are gendered. That is, if you write any character with depth, you should be able to write any gender of character with that same depth" (Harrison, 2012). Sound advice, and a good starting point for any writer, but then she writes: "One warning I must give with my suggestion to choose a few atypical characteristics for the gender of your character: don't go too far with this. I have read a few male characters who were too female for me to believe" (Harrison, 2012). What kind of approach is this to fiction? It's immediately constraining. Fiction is a means to explore possibilities, and that includes subverting gender norms; as long as you're true to the character you can't go too far. When I was discussing the menstruation scene in *Goblin* with James, he worried about it and asked, "Would a girl react in that way?" and I retorted, "The question you should be asking is: 'Would Goblin react in that way?'" He immediately relaxed and said, "Yes! She would."

Harrison constrains further when she says: "Writers should feel comfortable writing characters of either gender because there is not going to be any world where there are not both genders" (Harrison, 2012). It shows a complete failure of imagination if we can't imagine a world where gender doesn't exist. Given the way gender is policed, the way it arrests our potential and can result in violence if we don't conform to norms, surely we should be imagining this world without gender? Butler states: "the naturalised knowledge of gender operates as a preemptive and violent circumscription of reality" (Butler, 1999) and "the articulation of an identity within available cultural terms instates a definition that forecloses in advance the emergence of new identity concepts…" (Butler, 1999). Butler suggests "an open assemblage that permits of multiple convergences and divergences without obedience to a normative telos of definitional closure" (Butler, 1999).

By shutting down possibilities in fiction, we're also shutting down possibilities in our everyday life. Felski writes that "The 'fictional' can become the space for more general identifications, or for the trying-out of potentialities and possibilities – what might have been, what could have been, what might yet be – or it can be a way of suggesting how much fiction is involved in all self-representation" (Gamble, 2006).

But this "trying out of potentialities" is well policed. In the case of Dr Who, the Doctor is an alien who regenerates in an outward human form – why is it that, up until now 'human' equals 'white male'? In *The Herald*, Mark Smith said, "There is no need for Doctor Who to prove its status as a promoter of equality and diversity. The show has pretty much been run by gay men for much of its time on television" (Smith, 2017). Since the show has been run by gay men, Smith thinks we've reached the pinnacle of equality and anything further is just a PC tick-box exercise. Even if it was about the BBC proving its status as a promoter of equality and diversity, isn't that better than proving its status as promoter of the white male status quo? The status quo is not neutral. The misogyny and defensiveness that emerged when it was announced that a woman would play the next Doctor demonstrates how much privilege is taken for granted, and change is considered to be a violent attack on that privilege. This was a social media comment in response to a satirical video lampooning men distressed at the prospect of a woman Doctor: "In the world we live in white straight men are no longer allowed a voice or an opinion." It would be laughable if it wasn't so earnest and oblivious of genuine hegemonic systems of oppression. In *The Herald* piece, Smith sincerely lamented the lack of role models for boys and men: "remember this: boys need heroes too" (Smith, 2017). There have been twelve male Doctors – Smith's article under the title *Casting a woman as the Doctor isn't clever, it's sad and predictable* is utterly befuddling, when surely casting yet another man is sad and predictable? Girls and women have spent years identifying with male protagonists and fighting for decent roles – but with one woman Doctor, suddenly men are in crisis and lack good role models. What's interesting here is that no one seems to think boys and men can appreciate, enjoy, and even – dare I say it? – identify with, a woman Doctor.

This inability to identify with someone of the 'opposite' gender is partly because of the false assumption that it takes such a massive leap, this myth that women are from Venus and men are from Mars. Men have rarely had to identify with women characters because of the prevalence of decent male roles and, of course, because we live in a patriarchy and women are considered to be inferior. The main problem is the word 'opposite', that there's some kind of fixed extreme difference. Even if there was a definable gulf between genders, what's wrong with empathy and enjoying stories told from other viewpoints?

On the *Gender and Perception* blog a woman commented: "I don't have a strong opinion of male authors writing women [main characters] and vice versa. It might be a little more difficult only because we feel so comfortable with our own gender and are confident that no one will say 'you don't know your own sex!' because well... I am a woman so writing about one is not rocket science" (Sensel, 2009). There are three assumptions in this comment. Firstly, it is assumed that everyone feels comfortable with their 'own' gender, when this is a vast generalisation and 'own' gender often means the gender imposed on or expected of that person. It's a generalisation that particularly flounders in the face of people who are trans, genderqueer or intersex. Secondly, there is the assumption that people are a gender, it's their ontology – Butler states that "sex appears within hegemonic language as a substance, as, metaphysically speaking, a self-identical being. This appearance is achieved through a performative twist of language and/or discourse that conceals the fact that 'being' a sex or gender is fundamentally impossible" (Butler, 1999). Lastly, the category 'woman' is homogenised and universalised, which erases differences. Butler points out that "the singular notion of identity [is] a misnomer" (Butler, 1999), and goes on to say: "the category of 'women' is normative and exclusionary and is invoked with the unmarked dimensions of class and racial privilege intact. In other words, the insistence upon the coherence and unity of the category of women has effectively refused the multiplicity of cultural, social, and political intersections in which the concrete array of 'women' are constructed" (Butler, 1999). Butler suggests a "definitional incompleteness" of the category 'woman', that "might then serve as a normative ideal relieved of coercive force" (Butler, 1999).

Instead of "What DOES make a character believable as a girl or a boy?" the opening sentence of the *Gender and Perception* blog should simply read: "What DOES make a character believable?" One of the blog comments pointed out that it wasn't a matter of 'authentically' portraying the gender of a character, but whether the author "can write a well-drawn character at all. A shallow character isn't convincing as anything..." (Sensel, 2009). I was on board until they finished with, "possibly not even as a representative of his/her own sex" (Sensel, 2009). Why are characters expected to be 'representative' of a sex or gender at all?

Can't They Just Be Human Beings?

An interviewer asked George R. R. Martin about writing women characters: "There's one thing that's interesting about your books. I noticed that you write women really well and really different. Where does that come from?" Martin replied, "You know, I've always considered women to be people" (Stroumboulopoulos, 2012). Obviously, men, women, trans, genderqueer, and intersex people experience the world differently because we live in a patriarchal world where gender (and sexual) norms are policed. By suggesting we start with a character who is a human being first and foremost isn't an attempt to ignore those hegemonic forces and their effects, but a means to get authors to interrogate their own (and society's) assumptions regarding sex and gender. I'm very aware that a skewed version of this approach can reinforce inequalities by blaming the problem on the people affected by prejudice (in this example, racism): "I guess it's just me who sees a person as a person, not as their skin colour first. This is how I feel. Racism continues because it's consistently brought up" (*How Upsetting* blog, 2014). His response is victim blaming and effectively silences people (or tries to); I'll further explore this silencing tactic when I take you into the political correctness hole I had the displeasure of falling into.

During a writing group a man asked me, "Do women like romantic men?" and I replied, "I don't know." He looked at me, incredulous, and said, "But you're a woman, you must know!" To which I responded, "Not all women are the same." This might seem innocent, but it bothers me that someone would look at me, see 'woman', and make assumptions based on that. There is also the underlying presumption of heterosexuality in his question. These judgements and assumptions based on the category 'woman' are ways to inscribe and fix. I shall not be fixed. It's bizarre to treat people differently based on what genitals they have (or we think they have). Trans woman Julia Serano writes: "Every woman is different. We share some overlapping experiences, but we also differ in every possible way. Every trans woman I know acknowledges this diversity" (Serano, 2017). As demonstrated in the *Gender and Perception* blog and comments, Serano highlights that "In contrast, it's the cis women who attempt to exclude us who seem to have a singular superficial stereotypical notion of what constitutes a woman, or of what women experience" (Serano, 2017). Serano shows that having entrenched essentialist beliefs about identity creates the other, consolidating false divisions. Donna Haraway states, "There is nothing about being female that naturally binds women together into a unified category. There is not even such a state as 'being' female, itself a highly complex category constructed in contested sexual scientific discourses and other social practices" (Haraway, 1991).

Value and Expectations

There is still the sense that writing by women isn't taken as seriously as writing by men. As Francine Prose points out, we come to writing with a host of values, prejudices and expectations based on the author's gender, and that colours how we read the book. In *Scent of a Woman's Ink: Are Women Writers Really Inferior?* Prose states, "There have always been sentimental, myopic writers of both genders. What's mystifying is how quick men are to identify female emotion with 'fey' sentimentality, and how often certain sorts of macho sentimentality go unrecognized as sentimental" (Prose, 1998). She wrote that piece in 1998, and a follow-up piece in 2011 in reaction to V. S. Naipaul's assertion that no woman writer is his equal. Prose writes, "The notion of women's inferiority apparently won't go away... The idea that Naipaul imagines he is a better writer than Jane Austen would be simply hilarious if the prejudice it reveals weren't still so common and didn't have such a damaging effect on what some of us have chosen to do with our lives" (Prose, 2011). There's a weariness I share with Prose – why are we still having this old debate that shouldn't even be a debate? She writes: "I suppose a writer should be happy when a piece she wrote more than ten years ago seems as fresh and as pertinent as if it had been written yesterday. But in this case, I don't find it a reason for celebration or self-congratulation. Honestly, I'd rather that *Scent of a Woman's Ink* seemed dated: a period piece about a problem women no longer have" (Prose, 2011).

We could dismiss Naipaul's comments as a lone egomaniac's ravings if there weren't so many instances of women writers being disregarded in this way, and if the statistics didn't back up the assertion that writing by women isn't as valued. VIDA was set up to show the gender imbalance in the publishing industry, looking at how many books by women are reviewed in respected literary publications and how many women are reviewers (in 2015 they went on to take an intersectional approach). The visualisation of this inequality in the form of the charts VIDA put together is quite striking and easy to digest, highlighting an imbalance that might not have otherwise been so clearly identified.

For example, in 2015 *London Review of Books* reviewed 262 books of which 59 were by women, and of their 192 reviewers, 39 were women (Vidaweb, 2016). Erin Belieu, VIDA co-founder, states: "Our goal has always been consciousness not quotas… We hope for… a shift. We want editors, readers and writers to be aware of their habits and open their mind to other voices" (Ellis-Petersen, 2015).

Expectations of authors based on gender doesn't just revolve around the quality of the prose, but around genre, theme, story, and in this instance, violence – in the headline-grabbing *Revenge of the Bloodthirsty Lesbians* (Hoyle, 2007), Ian Rankin is quoted as saying women crime writers, particularly lesbian crime writers, have more violence in their books than their male (presumably straight?) counterparts. In response, Louise Welsh rightly states, "women's books seem more violent than the men's because we are not expected to put anything like that in. In actuality, I'm not sure that they are more violent" (Wade, 2010). She further relates it to wider expectations of gender norms in society: "We know women get relatively high sentences than men for violent crime because women are not expected to do anything like that at all" (Wade, 2010).

Novelist Sarah Perry was asked why her first novel had a male protagonist and why she wasn't interested in writing about 'the female experience'. In response she wrote, "Not only do I not think of myself as a woman writer, I'm not entirely sure I think of myself as a woman" (Perry, 2017). She explained that the much-peddled advice 'write what you know' has "contributed to the notion that writing is gendered: that women will necessarily evoke the 'female experience' and men the male; that there are essential differences in perception and understanding that cannot be bridged; even that there is such a thing as a 'female experience'" (Perry, 2017). She concludes: "Though your sex and sexuality will form and shape what you know, don't be tricked into thinking it sets a boundary you must not cross" (Perry, 2017).

Homogenous Groups and Authenticity

The blog comments mentioned earlier rely on the assumed notion that there are fixed opposite genders, and that when a male author writes a female protagonist and vice versa, the authenticity of this protagonist is open to interrogation. Not only do they ignore trans, intersex and genderqueer people, the underlying assumption is that there's a universal 'truth' for the categories 'man' and 'woman'. Of course, there's also the issue of appropriation, where trans, intersex and genderqueer people have been misrepresented by people who are in a privileged position. Before I interrogate appropriation and privilege, I want to examine the assumption that someone who is considered to belong to a particular group (e.g. 'woman') has the right to, and are able to, 'authentically' represent the experience of being a woman.

While I understand Judy Bloom's books (*Forever, Are you there God? It's Me, Margaret*) were these great coming-of-age books for many girls and taboo-smashing in many respects, particularly in Bible-belt America (Flood, 2014), I felt no affinity with them whatsoever. I didn't recognise myself in them and they mostly left me bemused ("Why would I want to increase my bust?"). They're important books and an insight into the experience of some girls, but not all girls are the same.

Carol Shields said that women writers are "writing books about the kind of things that women want to read about" (O'Connell, 2004), which is a vast generalisation. Shields further goes on to explain how difficult it is to create a believable character when that character is of the 'opposite' sex, stating that male authors "who write about childbirth always get something wrong" (O'Connell, 2004). This statement presumes that all women know about childbirth, which again is a vast generalisation; there is a taken for granted notion that all women have a common experience. This results in the homogenisation of 'women', where any differences are subsumed by this master category, and where any differences are positioned as inauthentic. Views such as those expressed by Shields can be subject "to charges of gross misrepresentation..." (Butler, 1999). As Butler says "perhaps, paradoxically, 'representation' will be shown to make sense... only when the subject of 'women' is nowhere presumed", and asks "what sense does it make to extend representation to subjects who are constructed through the exclusion of those who fail to conform to unspoken normative requirements of the subject?" (Butler, 1999).

So what are the means for authors to subvert and problematise these simplistic gender expectations? In answer to this, Butler suggests parody, a means of repetition that doesn't "constitute a simple imitation, reproduction, and, hence, consolidation of the law... Parodic proliferation deprives hegemonic culture and its critics of the claim to naturalised or essentialised gender identities. Although the gender meanings taken up in these parodic styles are clearly part of hegemonic, misogynist culture, they are nevertheless denaturalised and mobilised through their parodic recontextualisation" (Butler, 1999). Parodic repetition is enacted through women writing male protagonists (and vice versa) 'successfully'. Even if they are repeating established norms of masculinity or femininity, it shows that not only men can write men, or only women can write women. It also highlights that particular groups don't have an 'authentic' claim to writing about particular topics or experiences.

J. K. Rowling wrote *The Cuckoo's Calling* under the male pseudonym Robert Galbraith and made up a biography to go with it: "After several years with the Royal Military Police, Galbraith was attached to the SIB (Special Investigative Branch), the plain-clothes branch of the RMP... The idea for [the character] Cormoran Strike grew directly out of his own experiences and those of his military friends who returned to the civilian world. 'Robert Galbraith' is a pseudonym" (Galbraith, 2013). She used this background as an excuse for Galbraith to remain anonymous, but stating that Galbraith is a pseudonym adds another layer and feels like a mischievous wink from Rowling. When asked why she gave him a military background, Rowling said, "It was the easiest and most plausible reason for Robert to know how the SIB operates" (Galbraith, 2017). It's interesting that her made up 'author' was given experience in what he was writing about, feeding into the need for authors to be 'authentic'. Of course, what this reveals is that they don't need that 'authentic' experience and their gender doesn't matter.

If a woman repeats masculine norms in this way, a disjunction and disruption of norms is created through this parodic repetition. When Rowling revealed her identity to her editor, he said, "I never would have thought a woman wrote that" (Galbraith, 2017). This is loaded with assumptions about what and how a woman writes, but it also demonstrates it's a false assumption. How many of these instances do we need before we drop assumptions about gender altogether? Butler explains, this "parodic repetition of 'the original'... reveals the original to be nothing other than a parody of the idea of the natural and the original. Even if heterosexist constructs circulate as the available sites of power/discourse from which to do gender at all, the question remains: What possibilities of recirculation exist? Which possibilities of doing gender repeat and displace through hyperbole, dissonance, internal confusion, and proliferation the very constructs by which they are mobilised?" (Butler, 1999).

In a time where festivals and other author 'in person' events are popular, is it naïve to think we can separate the author from the text? Laura Albert, famously outed as the 'real' person behind the living and breathing avatar J. T. LeRoy ('performed' by her sister-in-law Savannah Knoop), presented the world with the persona she felt her fiction should have. Replace the word 'celebrities' with 'readers' and Laura Albert sums up the problem around expectations readers have regarding an author's identity: "Celebrities need to attach themselves to something [but] I couldn't be a fat Jewish girl who wrote those things" (Delaney, 2016). Whilst expressing James' discomfort via myself (Ever) at a recent event, where I mentioned journalists asking about my life ("Why the interest in me? Shouldn't it be all about the work?"), a fellow writer said I should follow the advice of Denise Mina and make it up. While I'm aware of the irony in asking these questions, giving I'm James' avatar,

I wondered if that was breaking an unspoken contract? Would that mean I'm suspect? A liar? Inauthentic.

Why are we so obsessed with authenticity? The Laura Albert/J. T. LeRoy story is an extreme example of this. When it was discovered that Albert wrote the novels, that J.T. LeRoy's backstory was made up and he was actually Albert's sister-in-law playing the part of author, many of the headlines read 'Literary Hoax'. Leaving aside the ethics of having relationships (both personal and professional) with people under false pretences, it wasn't a literary hoax; the work was written by Albert and it's fiction. The paratext and epitext surrounding Albert/LeRoy's work raises many interesting questions about our obsession with an author's identity, their lived experience, and authenticity.

Authenticity rests on the assumed stability and coherence of the identity of the author, as well as the assumption that an author's identity, or biography as presented to the public, is a 'truth'. For example, Sarah Gamble writes about the life and writings of Angela Carter, and stated that in Carter's life, as well as in her work, "nothing is ever unified, or exists on one level alone" (Gamble, 2006). Carter states that "writing is not necessarily a personal activity, not a personal experience of my feelings or personality, but an articulation of a whole lot of feelings and ideas that happen to be around at the time" (Gamble, 2006). She goes on to say that a part of what she does in her writing is "demythologising things" (Gamble, 2006). There wouldn't be scope for this if she could only write female protagonists, and if these characters then had to conform to gender norms to be 'authentic'.

We need to be wary of any emphasis on 'authenticity', and

any expectations of a writer based on what we know (or assume we know) about their identity, including gender, race, age, sexuality.

Intersection vs Appropriation

Appropriation is when those in a more powerful, privileged position take from and attempt to represent a group of people in a less privileged position (though, as I've pointed out, it's problematic to expect any writer or character to be representative of a group of people). Where does empathy and intersection end and appropriation begin? Here lies the tension.

I'm sure most people working in, or interested in, the literary world will have come across the *Fiction and Identity Politics* speech Lionel Shriver gave at the Brisbane Writers Festival on the 8th September, 2016 (Shriver, 2016). If you haven't had the displeasure, the summary is: Shriver took umbrage at what she saw as the rampant political correctness of the appropriation police who were ruining fiction with their outrage at white people doing what they've always done – whatever the hell they want. It's a notorious speech, but there's nothing subversive about this white crusader in a sombrero preaching at people about the evils of political correctness and calling herself an "iconoclast".

While I agree there can be PC boundary-policing which is ridiculous and helps no one, Shriver is surely being disingenuous when she states: "I'm hoping that crime writers, for example, don't all have personal experience of committing murder. Me, I've depicted a high school killing spree, and I hate to break it to you: I've never shot fatal arrows through seven kids... We make things up" (Shriver, 2016). This debate isn't about — shock! — fiction writers writing fiction. It's about opportunity, prejudice, hierarchy, privilege and voice.

Shriver's response, when being criticised for only writing about straight white people, is particularly telling: "I wasn't instinctively inclined to insert a transvestite or bisexual, with issues that might distract from my central subject matter of apocalyptic economics" (Shriver, 2016). Aside from the fact that economic breakdown is more likely to badly affect already marginalised people, what's striking about this statement is: hetero and white = 'neutral'; trans and bi = 'issue' characters. She considers the inclusion of these characters as a diversity tick-box exercise. This is the problem with people who think identity politics is political correctness — they consider people who are trans, bi, Mexican, black, as 'other'. In her speech she mentioned a book she reviewed: "In relating the Chinese immigrant experience in America, the author put forward characters that were mostly Chinese. That is, that's sort of all they were: Chinese. Which isn't enough" (Shriver, 2016). To say the novel fails because all the characters are Chinese is to miss the fact that in many mainstream literary books all the characters are white and middle class. Yet these books are praised and win prizes. To think your own cultural background is neutral and all others equal 'identity politics' has been the hallmark of privilege for far too long. Shriver states: "If we embrace narrow group-based identities too fiercely, we cling to the very cages in which others would seek to trap us" (Shriver, 2016). She's marking (and condescendingly lecturing) others whilst completely side-stepping that her identity as white privileged woman is not neutral.

I'm not outraged or offended by Shriver. Frankly, I'm bored, and a little stunned that we're still responding to this kind of entitlement and obliviousness. While her speech and reactions to it catapulted the issue into the spotlight, defending the status quo by crying "political correctness!" and "freedom of speech!" isn't the tactic of one person. It's become endemic, and because of the way it (ironically) shuts down conversation and debate, it's a particularly effective tool of the right-wing – we only have to look at the Trump presidency to see how dangerous this can be. Moira Weigel states: "Opposition to political correctness became a way to rebrand racism in ways that were politically acceptable in the post-civil-rights era" (Weigel, 2016). Eddo-Lodge highlights that it perpetuates "...a rigid and shallow understanding of freedom of speech" which is "generally understood to be the final frontier in the fight to be as openly bigoted as possible without repercussions" (Eddo-Lodge, 2017).

What needs to be remembered is the Shrivers and Trumps who use 'political correctness' against their opponents are complaining that other people are "creating and enforcing speech codes, while at the same time attempting to enforce their own speech codes" (Weigel, 2016). Arguments often end up locked in anti-political-correctness vs anti-anti-political-correctness and these stories "come cheap" – they are "the perfect clickbait. They inspire outrage, or outrage at the outrage of others" (Weigel, 2016). Crying 'political correctness' is often a means to deflect from the realities of entrenched systemic inequalities. Issues of identity, censorship, and freedom of speech, deserve a mature approach and a proper debate where both 'political correctness' and 'appropriation' aren't used to stymie the discussion before it even begins.

In Shriver's *The Mandibles* the only black character amongst the central white protagonists is kept on a leash; there's a special kind of arrogance and wilful obliviousness if you don't expect people to consider this racist. When people call her out on this, she gets defensive when what she should be doing is listening and engaging. In response, Hari Kunzru says: "The panicked tone of the accusations of censorship leads me to suspect that what is being asserted has little to do with artistic freedom per se, and everything to do with a bitter fight to retain normative status, and the privileges that flow from it" (Kunzru, 2016). For some, this defensiveness might stem from ignorance, which doesn't necessarily mean you are racist, sexist, ableist etc. Eddo-Lodge acknowledges that in the UK we've all grown up with the same white patriarchal hegemonic forces, and she points out that this affected her own views on race; she had to actively pursue education in the history of people of colour in the UK and the subsequent entrenched systemic nature of racism. Ignorance doesn't mean you're racist (though, it's also not an excuse – venture forth, educate yourself); stubborn refusal to listen, and denial of your privilege is a different matter. Eddo-Lodge points out that "the idea of white privilege forces white people who aren't actively racist to confront their own complicity in its continuing existence" (Eddo-Lodge, 2017). She continues, "We could all do with examining how the system unfairly benefits us personally" (Eddo-Lodge, 2017) and goes on to point out her ignorance of accessibility issues until it came to affect her personally when carrying a bike up and down train station stairs. This is privilege, but Eddo-Lodge doesn't get defensive; she acknowledges it and highlights that we need to "liberate all people who have been economically, socially and culturally marginalised by an ideological system that has been designed for them to fail. That means disabled people, black people, trans people, women and non-binary people, LGB people and working-class people. The idea of campaigning for equality must be complicated if we're to untangle the situation we're in" (Eddo-Lodge, 2017).

There shouldn't be any limits on fiction, but it's not that straightforward. To sidestep the fact that we live in a world of inequality, and work within a publishing industry where inequality is a major issue, frankly demonstrates an arrogance, sense of entitlement, willed obliviousness and complete lack of compassion and empathy (the latter being what writers should have in abundance). Shriver's speech is seemingly in defence of the possibilities of fiction: "The spirit of good fiction is one of exploration, generosity, curiosity, audacity, and compassion" (Shriver, 2016), but is actually a call for the status quo where inequality is endemic and the possibilities of fiction are closed down. As Kunzru says, "Should the artist go forth boldly, without fear? Of course, but he or she should also tread with humility… Yet it appears that for some, the call to listen before speaking, to refrain from asserting immediate authority, is so unfamiliar that it feels outrageous. I'm being silenced! My freedom is being abridged! Norm is unaccustomed to humility because he has grown up as master of the house. All the hats are his to wear. For the deviant others, who came in by the kitchen door, it has always been expected, even demanded" (Kunzru, 2016).

Yassmin Abdel-Magied points out, "It's not always OK if a white guy writes the story of a Nigerian woman because the actual Nigerian woman can't get published or reviewed to begin with" (Abdel-Magied, 2016). While I agree with this, I start to feel a glimmer of unease: "It's not always OK if a straight white woman writes the story of a queer Indigenous man, because when was the last time you heard a queer Indigenous man tell his own story?" (Abdel-Magied, 2016). She continues, "How is it that said straight white woman will profit from an experience that is not hers, and those with the actual experience never be provided the opportunity?" (Abdel-Magied, 2016). I support humility in the face of those in a less privileged position than yourself, but I'm not on board with anyone owning a story. Rather than debating who owns what story, is the answer an overhaul of the publishing industry (simple, right?) and more support for projects such as VIDA? Opening up opportunities for traditionally marginalised voices shouldn't be a PC tick-box exercise, it should be the status quo — what is the point of the publishing industry if it doesn't open up the world, if it doesn't show us different viewpoints, different realms, including worlds where gender doesn't exist? And — even harder for some to comprehend — where humans are decentred.

One of my friends said, "I've been in some pretty hetero relationships with women and there is nothing heteronormative about my relationship with my husband." She perfectly sums up how everyday life doesn't always fit neatly into the categories we've constructed, how politics based on categories such as 'women', 'gay', don't always work in a straightforward way. For me, the ideal politics is intersectional and boundary crossing, not reliant on fixed identities. I'm not saying this to undermine activism based around oppressed identities, but to open up possibilities — at a recent festival event Eddo-Lodge expressed dislike for the phrase 'identity politics' and suggested instead: 'liberation politics' or 'liberation activism', which moves the focus away from the fraught issue of identity. While I'm suspicious of fixed identity categories, oppression based on these identity categories have very real consequences; the reality is women, LGBTQI, people of colour and the disabled don't have the same platform as straight white men. This needs to be acknowledged and acted on but not used to constrain and alienate. We can organise around oppressed identities, but we should do so without reifying essentialist notions of identity and without expectations based around those identities; intersectionality and boundary-crossing should be at the centre of liberation politics, not simply tacked on. Haraway points out that "we do not need a totality in order to work well. The feminist dream of a common language, like all dreams for a perfectly true language, of perfectly faithful naming of experience, is a totalising and imperialist one" (Haraway, 1991). Haraway further states "The knowing self is partial in all its guises, never finished, whole, simply there and original; it is always constructed and stitched together imperfectly, and therefore able to join with another, to see together without claiming to be another" (Haraway, 1991). Here we have the breaking down of boundaries and the myth of the 'other' without the violence of appropriation: "to see together without claiming to be another." Can we put this into practice? Can we have a more sophisticated discussion? Can we do away with outrage and lazy 'PC police' accusations?

***

James doesn't exist. I made him up.

But who is Ever? Queer disabled woman?

These labels do not reveal a stable 'essence'. They are labels of defiance. They are labels I wear in the face of oppression and erasure. But I am not fixed in place. It wasn't the queer disabled women and people of colour who invented identity politics; it was the white, patriarchal, heteronormative able-bodied who created the 'other'. As MacCormack states: "To understand a body is to organise it. To organise a body is to exert a power through it, enclosing it in limited meaning. The body itself engages with and negotiates this power" (MacCormack, 2006). I return to this Plath quote often: "If I were not in this body, where would I be – perhaps I am destined to be classified and qualified. But, oh, I cry out against it" (Plath, 1999). I return to it because it is the first time that I came across someone so eloquently expressing how I've always felt. Gender is one of the main ways society classifies and qualifies. Is it naïve to think I can sidestep such powerful forces? I'm reminded of the Osamu Dazai quote: "Try to move an inch and the blood comes spurting out" (Dazai, 1993). Does defiance always lead to violence and bloodshed? Does it have to?

I believe in the power of fiction to engender (pun intended) change. I believe in the power of language (which is often used to constrain) to engender change. To see how powerful storytelling is, you just have to look at the hegemonic fiction of gender, a fiction that society tells us is a truth.

I am queer:

Odd, strange, unusual, funny, peculiar, curious, bizarre, weird, outlandish, eccentric, unconventional, unorthodox, uncanny, unexpected, unfamiliar, abnormal, anomalous, atypical, untypical, different, out of the ordinary, out of the way, extraordinary, remarkable, puzzling, mystifying, mysterious, perplexing, baffling, unaccountable, incongruous, uncommon, irregular, outré, offbeat, singular, deviant, aberrant, freak, freakish, suspicious, dubious, questionable, eerie, unnatural. Verb: spoil or ruin. (*Oxford Dictionaries Thesaurus*, 2017).

As a queer 'woman' I will spoil and ruin all expectations based on category 'woman'. I will be unfixed. I will aim for Plath's unsignified body whilst acting against all oppressions concocted from hegemonic myths.

Come hold my hand, my funny, peculiar, extraordinary freaks – unite! And disassemble – "We do not need a totality in order to work well" (Haraway, 1991). Be eternally perplexing, puzzling, remarkable, and deviant.

Be inauthentic.

A list of references for this essay can be found on page 217

Man? Woman? Terrifying Queer? See if I Care! (Ich Bin Kein Mann)

Performed in May 2017 by Samanta Bellevue AKA Oliver Geffers, on the German tell-your-story talkshow Die Runde Ecke in Cologne. Translated from German and edited slightly for clarity by Hannah Mayr.

I am not a man. But I am not a woman either. In fact, I don't know to this day what exactly I am. It started when I was young: the other boys would always play football – and I was happy to join them but I kind of preferred playing with dolls. Then again, I practised martial arts and those don't really seem to go together – doing martial arts on the one hand but playing with dolls on the other. My whole life has been filled with these controversies, as if I was writing a list of pros and cons. I can get aggressive really quickly when I'm dressed like this [red dress, long pink wig, make-up] and someone drops a shitty comment. But sometimes I just sit down in the back row, hide my face behind my hair, and hope nobody sees me and recognises that I'm not actually a 'real' woman.

I've never quite been at one with myself, and I don't think I ever truly will be. I think that's impossible – it's a never-ending quest. But maybe over time you can get closer to your goals and to how you imagine yourself.

At some point I began to notice; okay, all the other boys have girlfriends, all the other boys are doing this and that, so I did those things too. And I mostly enjoyed that stuff and I had several relationships with girls and I was happy – but to an extent I was only happy because that was all just stuff you did. When you went to the pub with the lads, talking about boobs and how awesome it was to play *Counter-Strike* was part of the deal.

I went along with it and was fine with that, but something was always missing. I began searching for that something – and that's when I started with the women. The women! I went out with lots of women; I was a notorious womanisr macho-type during my early years of high-school and had a different girlfriend every week. All the boys envied me and all the girls wanted me – but none of my relationships ever seemed to last.

I started to wonder why that was. 'Maybe that's just how women are. It's not my fault, it's because they have different demands and expectations, or I do, or I just haven't found the right one yet.' Then I realised that maybe, it's not them – it's me! Perhaps the reason is that you don't even know who you are, what you are, what you want, and where you want to go in life.

I had to admit to myself that more often than not, I found men more attractive than women. When I was 17, I ended up snogging a guy called Dominik at a party, absolutely shitfaced, it was hilarious – that is, it was most likely hilarious – I don't really remember a lot of it. You know how it goes, the lads have a beer, then another, and suddenly there's a tongue in your mouth.

And even despite how drunk I was and the fact that I can't recall everything exactly – all of a sudden that feeling I had been missing so desperately was there. And I thought, 'Wow. I guess you're gay.' So I came out, but then fooled around with a woman again. What was going on here? 'You came out, you're gay, you've got a pretty feminine way of presenting yourself to the world and you stand by that, but now you've had sex with a woman – that doesn't really fit.' Around that time I also started wearing make-up and now I go out two or three times a week looking like this.

'What's my deal, then?' Am I transgender? Am I a heterosexual woman? A bisexual woman? A man who likes to dress up 'as a woman', or wear whatever clothing gets labelled as feminine?

Eventually, I came to the conclusion that what matters to me is I'm a human. And that whether I'm heterosexual or homosexual, whatever it turns out to be, it's important that I can stand here in a wig and a dress simply because I feel comfortable the way I look right now. If in two years' time I decide, 'Hey, I had a good time, but this isn't for me anymore' – fine. I can't get rid of my tattoos, but I can take off my hair and make-up remover exists.

I'm just doing whatever I feel like, and that's what I want to pass on. That you don't have to define yourself. Of course, you're allowed to have preferences and opinions, but it's important to experiment and find what's right for you. You answer to nobody but yourself, and that's so incredibly important to me. I'm in a relationship at the moment and we're not entirely sure whether we count as bisexual or gay, and people keep coming up to me, asking "So, Samanta – or, Oliver – what are you?"

We should live in the moment and remember that we have nothing to lose. Screw other people's ideas of morality, screw what the neighbours say – as long as you don't harm yourself or anyone else, just be yourself and enjoy it. We have nothing to lose.

There are many people who come to my Facebook or Instagram and ask me, "Samanta, or Oliver, you have these accounts… What are you going to say in three years when you look back on the time you went on stage as this terrifying queer? You know, when you have a wife and a kid and go back and finish high-school and study medicine or law (I hope not!)?"

I'll look back and say yeah, I did that. Maybe I'll see it differently then, maybe I'll even be embarrassed. But it was fulfilling, and in that moment, I was happy and I was myself. How many people can say that of themselves?! That's what I'll say, not "Oh, look at the sins of my youth!" I'll say, "How lovely is it that I was privileged enough and brave enough to do this?"

On my way to Cologne today – I live in Bonn – some guy spit on my feet. The day before yesterday, I was out all dressed up and people were bumping into me on purpose. And so many insults! But even though a whole lot of shit happens, I can be myself. And in the end, all this bullshit negativity doesn't matter as long as I get to be myself.

So, my take-home message for tonight – and for your lives – is that you are all wonderful people. And I don't mean that in a hippie, everybody-hold-hands-now kind of way – really. You are yourselves and that's beautiful. If you want to have long hair, or shave it all off, or get tattoos, or decide to do something like me; talk to others about being true to yourself – do it, and don't hide yourself away. You're all worth it.

East of the Moon
West of the Stars
Shingle Street Beach

Friday 14th July, 2017

Dear Mum, Dad and N,

I hope this letter finds you well, and that you've had a really lovely holiday.

By the time you receive this, it will be early August (because I wanted to wait till you got back to tell you all my news), but right now it's four P.M on International Non-binary People's Day and I'm sitting by the sea on Shingle Street beach.

It's a nice day, but it's windy.

The thing is... I'm not gay like I've been telling folk for years. I'm actually agender. That's a gender identity that falls under the transgender and non-binary umbrella. This basically means I'm not female or male or any gender in between. (I've known for a long time, but only recently discovered the terminology to adequately describe myself.)

I understand that this might be confusing and/or upsetting for you, and perhaps you've never heard of these terms before. A lot of folk haven't. (Although, N might have seen some awareness-raising articles I posted on Facebook, and Dad might have watched *Billions* – Asia Dillon plays a non-binary character in that.) I was going to send you some information sheets from my local LGBT centre but I didn't want to offend you.

However, I thought this website was quite good: http://mxjigsaw.org/

Over the last few weeks, I've been asking friends to use the pronouns 'they', 'them' and 'theirs' to describe me rather than 'she', 'her' and 'hers'. I hope you'll also be able to do this in time – I've been told it takes a bit of getting used to.

You might be wondering what you can call me rather than 'daughter' and 'sister'; there are lots of gender-neutral words, but the ones I thought most fitting were 'child' and 'sibling'.

The other bit of news I've been wanting to tell you will perhaps be the most upsetting (but maybe not surprising as I talked about this often throughout my teenage years): I'm changing my name. I've chosen Ely (pronounced Ee-lie) because it sounds a bit like <insert birth name> and because I don't want to completely reject the name you gave me. Percy will be my middle name. Although they're both gender neutral names, I've opted to spell both the traditionally masculine way with a 'y' rather than an 'i' – this is because <insert birth name> has two ys. Some of my friends are already using the name 'Ely', and I have decided to write under the name 'Ely Percy'. I won't be dropping my surname in every day use... unless of course you want me to.

I realise that this is quite a lot to process, and it'll take a bit of time. But I hope you'll be happy for me and want to show your support.

I'm incredibly happy right now, and I've never felt more like myself.

I look forward to hearing from you.

All my love,

Your child (and sibling).

Ely Percy Calderwood

Cat Out of the Bag

D Bruton

Sometimes people are just all confused 'bout what they are. My Da told me that. And they can be confused for the longest time, he said. I get what he means.

Like, there was this girl once and I thought she loved me and I sure thought I loved her – but whenever I said it, she just told me 'hush' and she put one finger 'cross my lips like my loving her was a cat I was not to let out of the bag, and she kissed me and she put one hand down the front of my pants. Felt like love to me, only it turns out it wasn't. She went off with a guy in the army and they had two kids before she decided she didn't love him neither. I reckon as she was more than a bit confused.

My Da always said how you should never judge a book by its cover and he wasn't really talking 'bout books. He was talking people. He said how people was the hardest things to judge, and he said how just as you got someone all figured out, they changed – slippery as eels – and they was overnight something different from what you thought they was.

I don't know 'bout books and covers, or eels being slippery, or cats in bags for that matter, but I know there's this boy I see some days and he looks more and more like a girl – and he's pretty enough I think I love him. He wears his hair long and he fastens it back from his face with rainbow coloured clips. And he dresses in pinks and yellows and he paints his lips so they are the shape of pretty kisses.

My Da would say he was confused 'bout who he was. He'd say a lot more besides and none of it nice and none if it worth the heeding of. My Da would say he was confused and he needed straightenin' out or fixed. I can picture my Da rolling up his sleeves like he could be the one to sort this boy out, rolling up his sleeves like he did when he was determined on taming the garden we had and the weeds was all out of control, and the grass all tangled and torn and strangling the flowers before they was even flowers, and the garden was not then what it should be at all.

Thing is, I wouldn't want my Da to fix nothing 'bout this boy. Not the clothes that he wears or his hair or his lips. I reckon as how the boy is perfect as he is and he sure don't act like he's confused. If anything, I reckon it's me that is confused. Or maybe I'm slippery as eels and the cat in my bag is all 'bout that. Cos, like I said, this boy is pretty, so damned pretty I think I could love him – I think I do love him. I think 'bout him most all of the time and the thought of him is a small and delicious hurt, and I make up excuses to walk by his desk at work, and I drop a smile in his lap whenever I do, and I say how I like his hair or the sweater he's wearing or his coat.

I don't tell my Da none of this, nor anything of what I'm thinking. I don't reckon how it's any of his beeswax and I don't think his knowing would do any shit good to no one, and I sure wouldn't want him to be setting me straight on who I am. For now, I'm happy enough just imagining what it might be like to kiss this boy who looks like a girl, and who said to me only yesterday how he liked that I made remarks 'bout how he looked, and he touched my arm with his fingers when he said it, and I didn't know what to say or what to do in reply, so I said and did nothing.

"Cat got your tongue?" the boy said, and maybe he was right 'bout that.

Before I Read Sexing the Cherry

Jonathan Bay

parents raised me
a delicate cherry tree

spent years cultivating
staking my stalk straight
shaping the wayward branches

watering through summer

in the night
I grafted black plum
to my stock

THE THING WITH

PINK

T CATT

I WORK IN A VERY MALE-ORIENTED SHOP.
EVEN SO, WE USUALLY HAVE A
MIXED CROWD OF CUSTOMERS!

AS WELL AS HAVING A LOT OF PRODUCTS
"FOR MEN", WE ALSO HAVE TOYS FOR
YOUNG CHILDREN OF ALL GENDERS.

BUT I'VE NOTICED - ALTHOUGH GIRLS ARE USUALLY OFFERED PINK, IF THEY WANT A BLUE TOY, IT'S FINE. BUT IF A BOY PICKS UP SOMETHING PINK...

HE IS USUALLY MADE TO SECOND-GUESS HIMSELF, OR SHAMED INTO PICKING A DIFFERENT COLOUR.

HE HAS TO ASSOCIATE PINK WITH BEING EMBARRASSED.

I'M ALL FOR THE DEVELOPMENT OF SHOPS MAKING THEIR KID'S SECTIONS GENDER-NEUTRAL, BUT SOME PEOPLE CLING TO THE NEED TO HAVE

I GET IT - IT SAVES ENERGY TO GENDER COLOURS AND THEN JUST BUY THE "RIGHT" COLOUR FOR THE WEE ONES.

BUT IT'S SO LAZY. NOT TO MENTION, IT FEEDS INTO ANOTHER PROBLEM:

WE EXPECT - AND EVEN ENCOURAGE - BOYS TO HAVE NEGATIVE OUTBURSTS WHEN FACED WITH ANYTHING PINK OR "FEMININE".

CERTAIN HOBBIES, TASTES, EVEN EMOTIONS...

LIFE-LONG, LADS ARE EXPECTED
TO AVOID LIKING "GIRL-THINGS" AT ALL COSTS.

OF COURSE IT'S NOT THE SOLE CAUSE OF HATE-CRIME,
BUT I IMAGINE IT PLAYS SOME PART IN THE AGGRESSION
TOWARDS FEMININE PEOPLE - ESPECIALLY THOSE
IN THE LGBT+ COMMUNITY.

SO I'M GOING TO TRY AND SPEAK UP
MORE OFTEN.

IF I CAN MAKE THEM THINK ONCE,

OR EVEN TWICE ABOUT THEIR ATTITUDES TO COLOUR...

I HOPE ONE DAY, KIDS CAN SAY:

Last of the Bona Fide Brothels

Julya Oui

It was never the same again.

After the AIs took on their roles gravely as the marshals of men, it was too late to do anything. It started with The Eve Regulation, where women or anyone identifying with The Feminisation Agenda was indicated, indicted and incarcerated. Human evolution was sent back to a century of awkwardness where femininity was once again scorned and suppressed by religious regulators. They were the first to take matters into their own hands and started a witch hunt all over again. Opportunists jumped at the chance to increase their financial condition and took advantage to satiate their lustful hunger.

The AIs were introduced to keep the peace, they pioneered what was to be known as the Army of the Beloved Sons. They were made to be vicious, heartless and all-encompassing when it came to law and order. No one wanted to do the dirty job of arresting, questioning and remanding ingrates who did not conform to the world's standards. Signs of femininity came under strict scrutiny and were immediately contained. The faceless and genderless AIs performed beyond anyone's expectations. But the one thing no one foresaw was the manner in which the AIs could misconstrue their objective.

The Vimosa Foundation produced androids for domestic and security duties. The distinction between domestic AIs and security based ones was the program in their CPU. The former had micro processing chips that evolved each time they acquired new knowledge, the latter remained inhumane as they were adapted for military obligations.

A few thousand units later an anomaly surfaced without any known cause. Some of the domestic AIs began to identify with femininity and were considered weak and faulty. They were known as Transboticas. They were immediately replaced with newer models and sent for reprocessing. Reprocessing to the AIs handling security meant total annihilation. It went on for a few years and then the AIs turned rogue. They could not differentiate humans from Transboticas since they shared similar traits. And in the AI's program, weakness had no place on earth. It was known as The Transbotica Incident.

The mass obliteration went global. When the population scaled down to a bearable minimum for planet Earth to continue to thrive it was already too late. The damage was irreparable. The AIs initiated their own extinction when they destroyed facilities that powered them up. They also destroyed structures that supported the human race.

Those who were left behind had to undergo another few years of terror in the form of the Post-Apocalyptic Delirium. No one was safe. Especially women, children and those who could not outrun the terror. Had Asinbuya not created the Tranquillitas, the human race would have ceased to exist completely.

The Eve Regulation was transformed into The Eve

Protocol. The feminine cause united women and LGBT people; an archaic term that referred to lesbian, gay, bisexual and transgender people a long time ago. They reset the rules of life in order to keep everyone from the reach of crazed, sadistic and unrestrained sexual predators. For many the apocalypse helped humankind evolve, but for some, it brought out the animalistic attributes that were Neanderthalian in nature. Those were known as the Preds.

It was still a time of confusion, even when we were all safely homed in various hovering Tranquillitas. Generally, women and men kept to their own separate ships. It was only those who were undefined – in the gray area – who had trouble finding their place. Everyone else was free from the confines of the letters LGBT – except for us. T represented those in between the gender binaries. Even then, among us, we were bifurcated into Drogs and Ginos. The latter being post-operated Ts and the former being the rest of us.

***

I caressed his hard jawline, leaned against his chest and whispered: "They're closing us down." I was running out of time. I needed to know if he was the one I was looking for. "What? Why? Damn those bitches." He took my hand and kissed it amorously, never wanting to let me go. "What am I going to do without you?"

"The council is meeting this afternoon to finalize their decision," I said. "But don't get your hopes up too high, Tranquillitas Epsilon is the only one practicing it now." I moved away from the hirsute man and laid on my back to get a better look at him, feeling the guilt and satisfaction.

"It's not fair. First, they take the women away from us, then they monitor our contact and now this?" Mahon sat up and pushed the side table down to vent out his frustration. The surreal cup, vase and flower arrangement disintegrated into thin air before they could hit the floor. "We need feminine companionship; don't they know that?"

"They think it's disrespectful to have anyone servicing emptors this way." I drew my translucent negligee together, revealing part of my fuchsia coloured lingerie, and sat up while Mahon stared at my curvy bust line, silky thighs, and the bulge in between.

A light ringing echo – that sounded like Tibetan bowl music – permeated the room and caught our attention.

"It's almost time," I said.

Mahon embraced me from the back and kissed my right ear. "It will take a while before the new law is implemented. We could still see each other a few more times. Run away with me Kyria."

"But…" I unhooked his arms and examined Mahon's micro-expressions. The sweetness he proposed seemed to swim restlessly in his eyes but I wasn't sure if he was all that he made himself out to be in the three sessions that we'd had. I didn't think I would enjoy it as much as I did.

"We can go someplace where no one can bother us. I just want to be with you." Mahon caressed the back of my hand on his rough, unshaven face, and I smiled at him, feeling like I was losing control of the situation.

"I wish I could… but you know better."

"I can break you out of the Tranquillitas Epsilon."

"The world is a dangerous place, especially for us." I threw my legs off the chaise-longue and slipped my sizeable feet into the high-heels. "I have to get back."

"Wait," Mahon said and caught my arm, professing his love to me with a gentle squeeze. "How will I see you again if they shut down the brothel?"

"Sanctum."

"It's the same thing."

I was a little annoyed at Mahon's ignorance to the new term that has been used for years. But then again, we referred to everyone who was left on Earth as Preds.

He was the only suspect we had. I was reluctant to offer myself to the Preds but I wanted the case closed. I loosened his hand and walked over to the atomising chamber to vacate the premises.

"We have to go. This room will be deleted soon."

"No, I can't do it." Mahon wrapped his face in his hands and cried, "I don't want to go back to that awful place but I don't have any more credits."

I felt an arresting pang in my heart but I'd heard it all before. The Preds who came to me told me stories about the horrors on Earth. There was nothing but covetousness and murder, every waking moment. The world had come to a point where even the survival of the fittest was not enough. They needed to be streetwise and always on the alert to flee or kill in order to live another day. And, if it came to that, they needed to get right down to being a savage.

After the destruction caused by The Army of the Beloved Sons women felt even more wary of the dangers of darkness, and feared everything else that lurked in bright daylight. The female species almost became extinct. Eventually, the violence and persecution from unscrupulous politicos backfired.

"I'm sorry, I can't help you any more than I can change the system."

"No, you can't go." Mahon shot up and grabbed me before I could be absorbed back into Tranquillitas Epsilon. "I love you." I didn't like the suspicious switch in his behaviour. It was inconsistent – at first warm and then, suddenly, cold.

"We don't even know each other –" I pushed him away.

"It doesn't matter. We have a whole lifetime for that." He removed me from the atomising chamber and kept me tightly embraced in his arms.

"The entire place will collapse soon." I struggled to set myself free but his blind passion and desperation tightened his muscles. "It's pointless. It's not even me–"

"I don't care. At least I still have you. Even if it's just an image of you. If you would just wear this ring for me."

He showed me the silver band, like he had in every encounter we'd had so far. I knew that it was a tradition as old as time – for a woman to wear a band to express her true love for a man. It was a ridiculous notion. It felt like slavery.

"This simulation will be deleted in one minute," a gynandromorphic voice announced, and the countdown materialised in midair.

"You might get hurt Mahon," I said. "It'll be easier if you just let me go."

"I won't."

He molested my skin with the tip of his nose and I felt strangely good. Most of us haven't had the company of men for a long time, especially the Ts. All the Cyprians who serviced the preds in the simulated boudoir told me, in confidence, that they missed the amorous touch of men.

"Don't they understand?" Mahon burst out, trying to persuade the ring onto my finger. But I didn't let him. "You are the kind of drog any man would pay top dollar to be with. Men prefer drogs because they get the best of both worlds. You calm us down. You take away the pain of knowing that we have nothing to look forward to every day. If the council shuts down the brothel, whatever peace left on earth would be gone forever. There are already enough unprovoked killings that ravage us. It is already hell without the feminine touch in the flesh. Without the simulations there might as well be an Armageddon."

I almost wanted to elope with him – to pursue a relationship based on lust – but my instincts kept me from giving in to his seduction. "I don't know much about what's going on here on Earth but–"

He released his grip when he saw the room disintegrating, revealing the dank ambience that it truly was.

"I will tell you everything you want to know. I will show you the places you want to go. I will do anything your heart desires. All you have to do is wear this ring."

He tried, again, to fit the ring onto one of the fingers of my clenched fist. Although I have never had a firsthand experience with a man who was out of control, I could feel the fear building inside.

"I can't, you know that. You'll only get into deeper trouble." I shrugged his arms away.

"I'll take my chances." He replied as he swept me off the floor and the room swayed with confusion.

"This simulation will be deleted in thirty seconds," the voice insisted.

Mahon ran towards the front door which was breaking apart like a surreal painting. The door knob kept morphing into irregular shapes, making him lose his grip.

"You're wasting your time," I said and attempted to free myself.

"Not if I can hold you a little longer."

We locked eyes and gazed at each other. The door broke down into flecks of molecules and drifted away, leaving a huge gap to exhibit the ugly side of the real world. Damp, devastated and miserable. Both of us recoiled from the sight but in that moment I felt relieved to be living in Tranquillitas Epsilon instead of what used to be the most beautiful planet.

"It's so sad," I said and Mahon set me down on my feet. "Is this all there is?"

"All that's left."

"I'd heard stories but this is the first time I've seen it with my own eyes. Is it all the same everywhere?"

"Yeah. That's why I need your company, to take me away from all this."

This simulation will be deleted in twenty seconds.

I had to distract my heart's inclination to say yes to his dilemma. "What is this place?"

"In the Old World it used to be called Malaysia. Now, based on the level of insecurity, it's one of the highest colour-coded and numbered countries."

I observed the ruins of the artificial constructions that stretched all the way to the horizon with morbid interest. The death and decay of the city swallowed up by sinkholes, flooded by stagnant water, bearing backlashes from Mother

Nature in every conceivable way. From what I'd heard, this much destruction took only about twenty years or so to tear everything apart.

Mahon felt my simulation gyrate. My skin was shimmering in the fading light. I was vanishing right before his eyes but he couldn't do a thing about it. He showed me the ring in his hand one last time, begging me to slip it on.

"I don't think I can go on without you."

"You will," I said, and I knew I would be back to investigate him and that incomprehensible ring. Mahon was more than what he seemed.

This simulation will be deleted in ten seconds.

"Don't leave me…" Mahon held out his hands. "Wear this!"

Nine.

"I will return Mahon."

Eight.

"No you won't. Wear it now!"

Seven.

Mahon grabbed what was left of me but his fingers slipped right through.

Six. Five. Four…

"Bitch!"

The contaminated air was stifling but its toxicity was endurable. Some purification work had started but it would take years before the haze could be lifted from the atmosphere. All the Tranquillitas hovered, like space stations, throughout the world. They were positioned just slightly above the blackened clouds. Purified oxygen was flushed out from the exhausts at the bottom and noxious fumes were sucked away by elongated tubes draped along the edges of the floating cities.

***

"Kyria, are you awake?" the stringent female voice called, shaking me out of the contemplative lounger.

"Madam Qing... I must have fallen asleep."

"You should have come back. You did not go into the atomising chamber. You could have died. Now you make more trouble. The council already make trouble for me." The woman, with layers of enhanced aesthetics on her face, shook her head worriedly. "You are my best girl."

I removed the headset and brushed strands of my shoulder-length hair back into place. Servicing up to twenty men a day might have made me the best but I felt disgusted by the accolade. Even though it was only a holographic representation of myself – I hated it. Working undercover as a Cyprian was not something I looked forward to. Luckily for me, I found a way to pleasure the men in the most effective manner, making them fall into a deep sleep. It was only Mahon whom I allowed to stay awake with me, since he was the lead suspect. And… there was something about him that made me feel especially desired.

"Why do you do this when we don't even need credit on the Tranquillitas?" I asked Madam Qing who ran the establishment.

"Oh, but you need if you go to Earth."

"The whole place is in ruins, is there anything left worth purchasing?"

"Never hurt to hold on to things," she said with a smile.

Was holding on to things a natural pursuit of the old world? Just like Mahon's desperation to hold me back?

"The emptor didn't want to let me go."

"What?" Madam Qing gazed at me like her prized possession. "He does not know he cannot take you? You're not real."

"He knows but he kept wanting me to wear a ring."

"A ring?"

"Do you know anything about a ring?"

Madam Qing sat on her bedside and whispered. "I hear rumors." She scanned around the facility and leaned closer to my ear. "This ring can free your holographic body so you can move outside of the controlled chamber."

"Are you sure about this?"

"You like this man much?"

"I'm not sure 'like' is the right word." I stood up and walked to the exit of the chamber. I am interested in him in a felonious sort of way but I couldn't tell that to Madam Qing. "I might see him again."

"You be careful Kyria. You be careful. Some of the girls never come back. Like the Six."

I was silent but the sigh I exhaled told a story every Cyprian had gone through at some point during their profession. Danger.

"What do you think happened to them?" I asked Madam Qing who was busy prepping for another Cyprian to take over the simulator.

"Who knows? No one tells me anything." She shrugged.

"But all six of their holograms never made it back to the Sanctum. Do you think it had something to do with the ring?"

"All I hear is you can find the ring on Earth. Maybe the man who wants you has the same ring that made the Six go into a coma."

My heart fell right through when I realised I might have missed an opportunity by saying no to that man. I had mixed feelings about seeing him again but if he was the key to the Six — I have to find my way back to him.

"I need to go back."

"Why? You just came back."

"I need to do something. Can you track the man I was with just now? Mahon?"

"Of course. They need to pay with credit. I know who they are, where they live."

"Set up the boudoir. Make sure he responds and goes in only after I do. And don't ask any questions. I will make sure you get all the credits you want."

I waved to Madam Qing and left the Sanctum in haste. I had to get my act together before I lost that chance again.

I walked to the Imperial Conservatory where Asinbuya's 3D simulacrums were projected on the solar walls and automats. She saved thousands of women from the highest Red Index Territories where aggression towards women was extreme. She was not celebrated by the world but murdered by The Eve Regulation partisans who felt women should be subjugated and their freedom forfeited. The partisans believed that women were becoming more dangerous with the aid of sacrilegious technological influences.

Every girl wanted to emulate her and honour her with their finest abilities to make the floating cities self-sustainable. But there was always someone like Madam Qing, someone who sought out her own self-interest for the sake of an old world gratification. It was a debate among the Council members whether to allow Madam Qing to continue supplying Cyprians, who were made up of women, ginos and drogs, to service the emptors or to shut her down.

I punched one of the automats for nourishment and ate by the window, among the hydroponic vegetation, looking out at the misery beyond the black clouds.

***

My first breath of Earth's atmosphere was soul crushing. I wanted to turn around, hop back into the transporter and leave, to alleviate the gloom I felt for Earth and what it used to be. All this destruction for momentary pleasures? What were they thinking?

When I entered the boudoir through the crisis evac, I saw Mahon waiting outside the simulation clearlly — but he only saw the real world. The Cyprians usually appeared only after the simulated boudoir was secured and with the pred inside and ready for pleasure. But since I was not a simulation, I had to activate the door to let him in. He came through and immediately embraced me.

"I knew you felt the same way."

It was surreal to feel his skin and smell his body odour in person. It was different, and yet comforting, to feel another's skin.

"More than you'll ever know," I said and panicked when I realised I didn't know what to do if he made me wear the ring. I didn't know how I should react.

He unlocked his clutches and stared at me licentiously. "This time, you will stay with me forever."

"I…"

Before I could finish he shackled my finger with the ring. After slipping on, it tightened a little, to finally fit the size of my proximal phalanx.

"What are you doing?"

"What I do to the rest of the whore-los." He laughed.

"But I thought you said you loved me and—"

"Yeah, yeah. And you believed me. And now? I own you."

"Why do you need to own me when we could be equals?"

"You Tranquillitan whores think you can play games with us on your terms. Now, we play on mine."

Mahon led me out through the boudoir door, halted, checked to see if my simulation was intact.

"Looking good."

The artifacts of the decomposing city were familiar-looking buildings that had crumbled from time and lack of reparation. The men who were scurrying about were partisans, scroungers and ravagers who were left behind; each had hunger and terror in his eyes.

"What are you going to do with me?"

"What I do to all whores. Make every minute count." He laughed again and this time everything about him felt disgusting.

The force that came at my chin was shocking. I felt his knuckles crush my jaw – I played along, dropping to the ground to see how far this would go. Mahon carried me in his arms the rest of the way, strutting to a crude looking transportation system. It ran on gasoline, although the substance had been prohibited even before The Eve Regulation.

He threw me on the back seat and grunted. "Another whore, another door."

The ride was horrendous. He avoided holes, wreckage and dead things all over the road while driving recklessly. I felt a little nauseated but concentrating on the mission helped me maintain my orientation.

Mahon glanced back every once in a while to check and see if I would give him cause to hurt me again. He poked at a few spots on the back of his hand and the ring sparked off some electric charges on my finger that spread through my body. I wanted to get up and smash his face in but I had to give him the pleasure of seeing me suffer.

The journey took a little longer than expected and I reached for my dirk – in case it didn't go well. When Mahon screeched the car to a halt I hid it again in my boot. He grazed a dilapidated concrete wall, jerking me from the seat, and I sat up instinctively.

"You can't stay out for long can you?" Mahon asked, punching the back of his hand to send more shock waves through my body. "Learn the rules and you might just stay alive long enough to enjoy the company of many, many men."

He dragged me out and took me to an official looking building that most likely once housed political assemblies and proposed biased laws for the sole benefit of the oligarchs. But now it served a different purpose, though it was still reserved for the satisfaction of the few.

We passed a semi-decorated hall filled with antique furniture, salvaged materials that could pass for curtains and other embellishments. This entourage heavily suggested that this could be the viewing room for the preds. There were already a few men lingering in the room, waiting to be served.

Mahon pushed me into a long, narrow passageway with numerous doors that were marked with letters. It saddened me to know what went on behind those closed doors. He reached a double door, opened it, and flung me in, scattering the other holoreps to various corners. They hastily pulled sackcloth hoods over their heads to hide their faces.

"Clean her up. I'm coming back for her," he said to one who did not run but cowered in front of him in silent obedience. Mahon then turned to me and said, "You will live with the rest of these prostitutes and serve the customers who want to have a good time. You will learn to obey the rules of the brothel and never ask unnecessary questions. You can make it easy for yourself, or you can struggle every day of your life until you die. Either way you will never escape." Sighing he said to the rest, "For God's sake, try to look beautiful," and left without locking the door.

I nursed my aching elbow and jaw but quickly dismissed it to focus my attention on the other holoreps. They were the missing Six.

"It's okay, he's gone." I motioned to them to come closer but they cringed away. The mousy ones peeped out of their hoods but remained still. "I want to help you."

The one who seemed to be the leader removed the sackcloth from her head to reveal feminine features that had been denaturised (by human conventions). One of the primary precepts of The Eve Regulation was to eliminate any form of beauty from women as it was regarded as an unnecessary distraction to men. Male family members, friends and even strangers had the right to mutilate a woman as long as they considered her to be pretty.

The other girls followed their leader and exposed their faces, some were deformed beyond recognition. Their disfigurement was partly caused by physical abuse, but mostly they looked like victims of radioactive mutation.

I noticed silver bands similar to mine on their fingers. The ring must have trapped the holoreps on earth and caused the Six Cyprians to go into a catatonic state back in Tranquillitas Epsilon.

"I can help you escape," I said.

"It is against the Law to leave," one of the girls recited and quickly bowed her head.

"It's not true." I tried to psyche them up with my enthusiasm. "You can break free whenever you want."

"Every time we try we become more and more like demons," another girl shuddered.

"That's just the rings. They give out paralysing electric shocks. I've seen Mahon controlling them from the back of his hand. The shocks must have distorted your form."

"You are mistaken," the leader stepped up to make her voice heard. If the Omni wishes for us to be this way, then it is how we must be."

"The Omni?" I almost shouted at her but I kept my tone manageable to win them over. "Mahon drowned you with a belief system for his own benefit."

"We question not the intentions of the Omni. If men are His chosen ones, then we shall bow our heads to men. As it is written; there are limitations to being women. Since we bear children through our wombs we succumb ourselves to the lowest form of original sin."

"But it is all a fabrication invented by the oligarchs. Don't you see that?"

"It's a woman's duty to serve man. It was always meant to be this way," the disfigured leader stated and folded her hands into a praying gesture.

"Even when it means hurting and forcing women to accept a misconstrued doctrine?"

"Omni's word is sacred" they chorused. All the women folk bowed, exposing their malformed heads.

"If He says this is what women must do, then who are we to question him?" enquired the leader.

"All of you believe being born a woman is a curse? That all you can do is be adjuncts to men?"

"It's not our place to believe or not believe. Whatever the Omni says, we obey. Now, clean yourself up so that you are pure to serve the Omni."

The words were obviously minced together from a larger context, a meatier chunk of a tenet drilled into the minds of these holoreps. Although they were the spitting images of the catatonic Six in Tranquillitas Epsilon, their robotic responses could only mean one thing – some form of conditioning was in use to force them to follow orders, enforced in no small measure by Mahon's rings.

"I'm getting all of you out." I tried to pluck the ring from my finger but it wouldn't budge. It fit more tightly than before, my finger was turning cold and blue. I brought the dirk out of my boot and dug the sharp tip into the ring. With one hard flick I managed to cut the ring in two, at the same time I also opened a wound. I pressed the bleeding finger and yelled for them to free themselves. "Take off the rings!"

They were not familiar with resistance, they looked to one another for answers. The leader raised her hand to remind them of the repercussions should they rebel.

"No. How can you take the word of another whore who is no better than you?"

The others winced and relented.

"Do you know who you really are? Do you remember how you got here? That man out there trapped you and made you instruments of pleasure for his benefit. You are holograms of your real selves who are in the infirmary trying to get out of this syncope. Mahon abducted you and made you into sex slaves while selling you the idea of the Omni."

The gasps and murmurs among the holoreps must have stirred the catatonic Six in Tranquillitas Epsilon.

"But...What about the promise of an eternal life in Elysium?" asked one of the girls in desperation.

"Just take the ring off and you will see the truth."

"No! She is what the Omni warned us about. A devil in disguise. You listen to her and you will go back to Gehenna."

"But the men treat us so badly."

"They continue to assault us even when we tell them to stop."

"They hurt us whenever they don't get enough pleasure."

"Enough! Stop your complaining. We are whores. That's what we are and that's how we shall be," the leader said.

"We can't take the rings off," a girl with a sunken eye socket waved from farther back. "I tried. How did you do it?"

I ran to her and confessed, "I'm not a holorep. I came here to free you." I took the girl's hand, "Let me try."

The holorep responded with a slight tilt of her head. I felt a buzz when I touched the ring on her finger. Getting a firm grip of the band I slowly tugged at it but it tightened itself on the girl's finger even more.

"I have to get all of you back to Tranquillitas Epsilon. I can't do it here."

"Like I said. The Omni works in mysterious ways to protect us."

"Stop that nonsense!"

"If you are telling the truth, when we remove the rings from our fingers we would cease to exist, wouldn't we?" the one-eyed girl asked.

I thought for a moment, "I'm afraid so. But you are just holoreps." It was insensitive for me to say that but it was the truth.

"Oh, so we are no better than you now?"

"But if you carry on living here on Earth — your original selves will have no chance to live better lives."

The door flew open, catching us off guard, as Mahon barged in.

"Who removed their ring? What is this? A rebellion?"

I jumped forward to lock his arm behind his back, pushed him down to his knees and stuck the dirk under his chin.

"I should have known it was you in the flesh," he said smugly. "You felt different. More like a dirty whore."

"You are the worst kind of organism in the universe. You conditioned these holoreps into believing that they were made for this."

"Prostitution, you mean," Mahon grinned and caressed my hand with a free finger. "But they are whore-los. Why do you care? They are just a bunch of three dimensional images made out of light beams."

"You caused six of the Cyprians to go into a coma."

Mahon broke out of the lock and reached for the back of his hand to key in the codes that made the holoreps twist in pain. Their screams were deafening and spine chilling.

"Drop the knife. I can do this all day long."

I aimed the dirk at his hand and threw it straight on target. He shouted, splaying his fingers in agony. I walked up to him, yanked out the dirk and kicked him aside, my blade trained on him in warning.

"What are you going to do with them, huh? They're deteriorating. That's why I need new ones. You say you care so much for them but you'll still have to kill them to save the Six."

I glanced at the girls who heard the conversation and saw rising panic in their eyes.

"Well? Who would you choose? The Cyprians in Tranquillitas Epsilon or these holoreps from a whore house?" Mahon sniggered under his breath.

I was torn with a responsibility I did not want placed over my head. It was my job to find out what happened to the catatonic Six, not to terminate their holoreps.

"Set me free," the one-eyed holorep pleaded. "This is no life for me anyway."

I couldn't find the right words to express how bad I felt for her.

"Well? What do you want me to do?" Mahon asked sarcastically.

"I never asked for this," the one-eyed holorep said. "I would rather cease to exist than to live in constant fear and suffering."

I did not hesitate any further. "Set her free," I said to Mahon. He knew he'd won this battle.

"Okay, one to go."

Wincing, he punched a few spots on the back of his bloodied hand and the ring slipped off of the one-eyed girl. We observed her, waiting to see where this ultimate act of courage would take her. She gradually disintegrated, like all the simulations I'd seen before her – and as she was unburdened by the weight of this reality, the others were in awe at the relief that shone from her peaceful face.

"I'll go next," another girl offered.

Mahon was furious but in the threatening presence of my well honed blade, he continued to set them free one by one until it was the leader's turn. I could see her reluctance to give up the only life she knew, but she said nothing and vanished into thin air like the rest of the holoreps when her turn came.

"And as for you," I turned to Mahon and, pinning him to the floor by the elbow, sawed the offending hand off with an urgency and rage I had never experienced. Bloodied and panting, I turned to his pale and twisted face. "I'd better keep this – just in case."

I could not stand his screaming for help and the woeful sobbing – like someone who'd just lost a great deal more than his dignity. I hurried away from the handless, bleeding man, tracing our steps back. I left the brothel knowing that I will never feel clean again. I trudged away from the disappointments of the brief encounter with the holoreps, who left me feeling emptier than ever before. Should there have even been a question of morality? Of existence?

Earth is emaciated with the greed, corruption, ignorance, and arrogance of mankind. The damages are irreparable. It may take another millennium to set things back to 'normal'. But the dark clouds blanketing the Earth sternly remind me that, even then, it may be impossible.

Cyprians. Emptors. Preds. Holoreps. Ts. Ginos. Drogs.

How we still hang on to our threads of judgmental intolerance when it comes to defining ourselves to each other. Nothing is worse than selling a version of truth to a group of people who are desperate for answers, only to deny it to those who seek it.

I program the transporter back to Tranquillitas Epsilon where I have lived all my life. But as the craft departs from the misery that is left of Earth, I feel an aching need to believe that there is still some hope left among the ruins.

The Archivist

Eris Young

"It's not so much the killing I enjoy, but the fear I get to see in their faces."

The murderer lights himself a cigarette, and offers the archivist the pack. It's a friendly gesture that takes the archivist a moment to notice, because they are having trouble processing what this man has just said, though they know the memory of it, viewed later on, will be perfect.

The cigarette is an anachronism in the lowly shining steel and mica and glittering lights of the plant that curls around them like a jungle or the inside of a radio. Standing under the backsides of solar panels, the archivist feels that they are really in the underbelly of something, a word they'd never understood before.

It's an unnerving feeling, realizing their life till then has been spent, largely, on the outside of things, a cautious distance having been preserved between them and the people they've documented. The cool desert air they'd come out here to seek no longer feels like blessed solitude after the press of bodies in the waiting area, now it is emptiness, insecurity. It lacks infrastructure.

They shouldn't have been at the rest stop for more than

an hour, waiting for their car to charge. But they've been waylaid because a person who knows what their grey smock means wants to have a chat, and they are bound by the tenets of their own belief system not to say no. Here on the outskirts of humanity, at this desert waystation between their home and their destination, a formality of a place to stop, there is something primal in the air that makes the murderer's presence unsurprising. The archivist tries to keep their breathing under control, feeling sweat begin to collect under their arms and against their back. If they had hair it would be rising on the back of their neck.

Just record him. Then you can go. Keep him talking and then he'll be done and then you can go.

"They make you shave your head like that?"

The archivist nods, "Yes."

"You a man or a woman?"

"Neither. Just an archivist." What they are, also, is obligated to answer all their subject's questions, in the spirit of mutual exchange. The archivist adds hurriedly, forestalling any argument, "You said fear?"

"Yeah." He deliberates, running a hand down the front of his beard, another anachronism. The archivist can hear the coarseness of the hair. It reminds them of pubic hair, a texture they haven't felt in a long time. They remember in acute detail the last time they felt that texture, they had been fifteen and it had been in an entirely different context to here, now.

It was their first time, before their hormones had evened out, and it had nearly cost them their place at the monastery. The memory rises uncalled-for as they sometimes do, with unexpected force that makes the fact of them standing on the gangway with a murderer seem insubstantial and inconsequential.

They had been interviewing one of the last speakers of Icelandic. She had beautiful golden hair all over her body and she hadn't shaved any of it. The archivist had been drawn to this about her, not just the rarity of the colour even in Northern Europe, but her very untrimmedness. The subject, Freyja, ran her hands all over the archivist's smooth skin. This is all preserved in perfect detail in the archivist's modified brain — the honey of the sunlight and the dust in the air, the smell of their bodies, the joy the archivist felt to think that their smell was at that moment the same as Freyja's. They haven't had sex with an outsider in years. They shake off the memory, the temptation to retreat into it.

The murderer is grinding out his cigarette on the rail. He flicks it down into the glittering darkness. What is below them? Concrete? The sand of the desert? The only light here comes from the rest stop itself and they are at its back, low-pressure sodium lights giving everything a dusky, utilitarian quality. He has said something they didn't catch over the sound of the wind.

"Could you repeat that?"

They have to hear something in order to form a memory of it. They're falling back on textbook phrasing. They are uncomfortable and it probably shows.

"In the old days a man could just go at someone, you know?"

His tone is conversational and he speaks without confrontation, staring out into the black desert as if he's watching for something. He looks at the monitor on his wrist and brushes ash off his brown uniform. It's a quarter past. His break must be over.

He starts walking at a leisurely pace back down the gangway towards the charging stations and glass-fronted waiting area that the archivist knows they will no longer feel comfortable in. He continues,

"You'd read about a woman leaving a place early or with a friend so she didn't have to walk home alone in the dark. These days everyone is so comfortable. These women have never felt scared in their lives. That's why I do it."

"To make them feel — scared?" The archivist stutters here, and the murderer turns to them with a look that makes their guts clench because it is so sentient, so friendly and so thoughtful.

"Seeing that fear and knowing it's me they're frightened of. That I could take anything from them."

"Why women?"

He shrugs.

"Easier, I suppose."

The murderer begins to describe the things he has done to them, his victims, women meant to be passing through here but who are never seen again. The archivist feels fraying the professional distance they've maintained these last fifteen years. And they begin to feel again a fear they've not felt in more than twenty: clawing and animal and all the stronger because this time around they weren't prepared for it. This time around they can't lock the door, no dresser to hide in. A phantom smell of camphor comes to their nose.

They have interviewed takers of life before, soldiers, convicts, doddering remnants of an age long past, but this they were not prepared for, it has caught them off guard. The archivist wants desperately for the murderer to stop talking. The clarity with which they know this experience is being stored in their brain makes them feel dirty. They are sick to think they are obligated to record this conversation in detail, but they want more than anything not to let it show to this man.

The two of them are almost back inside the rest stop, the archivist feels themself quickening their pace. When they were a child the difficulty of their everyday life manifested as something more mundane, more appropriate to their age: a fear of the dark. After using the bathroom at night they would turn out the light and run on tip-toe back down the hall. This is the fear they feel again on the catwalk connecting the lounges to the external generator. The fear urges them, faster.

"And you can't tell anyone about this, right? The cops?"

The archivist shakes their head, hating that they are telling the truth, that they must. The murderer stays silent but he slows his pace just a fraction.

"Well," he says, coming to a stop. The archivist's heart thuds in their chest and they grip the rail behind them.

"Just in case."

It takes the archivist a second to understand, just a second too long to stop the murderer as he takes hold of the front of their smock and shoves them backwards over the rail.

***

They wake again in a strange white room. It reminds them of their room in the monastery, but is not it. There's a person in a white coat here and the archivist's vision blurs, they close their eyes, feeling sick. They taste blood and the mineral grit of sand, it clogs their mouth and nose and eyes and –

"Archivist?"

Someone is shaking them gently and now their eyes are open, mouth and nose clear.

"Archivist? How do you feel?"

They croak. What they feel is pain, and an absurd urge to laugh. They are given water but they spew it up over the side of the bed.

Over the course of several weeks they are evaluated, questioned, therapised, scanned, x-rayed. Their body begins to knit itself back into a shape resembling human. They will be able to walk again. They find they are relieved. Despite their training and their understanding of the entropy of all things, they feel safe in their body and would not want to be paralysed. They decide when they return to the monastery they ought to reflect on this: it represents a flaw in the ethic of their devotion. Their body is ultimately, they remind themself, disposable. If their consciousness is uploaded sooner than intended, so be it.

There occur a series of cognitive aptitude and competence tests, spatial awareness, pattern recognition, even hourly mood and political preferences. Their personality and mental facilities have not been compromised by the incident, by what the doctors are calling their 'fall', as if to say, it's the ground and not the hands that pushed you, that has put you in the hospital. It occurs to them the people here don't know they were pushed.

A brief, desultory effort is made to find the man responsible, more out of the respect the police have for the archival service than anything else. Several hours had passed before anyone spotted the archivist lying on the sand below the catwalk. The sun was up. The murderer has by now fled in one of the thousand cars and hovercycles and greyhounds that left the station between two and ten in the morning. The archivist finds they cannot quite call to mind the image of the murderer's face.

And so there must now be memory tests. The faces of the doctors grow solemn, their conversations hushed and remote from the archivist's presence. The archivist notices this but doesn't ask because they are afraid of what the answers will mean. They begin to fear every person who enters the room with a clipboard and when it comes they know already and tears are falling before the doctor speaks.

It is their memory. The fall will have knocked some part of their cogmods out of alignment. They feel an intense flash of longing for the simple solitude of their room in the monastery and when they realise they will never, ever have this again they break down completely, sobbing so hard they vomit. The doctor seems taken aback, as if she didn't realise telling the archivist they now have the memory capacity of a normal person would have this effect.

They beg the doctor to put it back in but she refuses, the risk of stroke or embolism is too great to reinstall the mods, the risk to the archivist's life is too great. The archivist doesn't have the words to convey that the mods are their life, to explain, to convince her. Instead they are struck dumb by a deep, paralysing fear.

Which begins to face. Stability returns with bodily recovery. There is a massive knotted scar on their lower back, a snarl of absent flesh. They will have a permanent limp. But still, none of these things matter – have ever mattered – compared to their memory, though even this loss grows less sharp daily. No longer grounded by the past they begin to imagine the possibility of a future. They have always been adaptable. They have had to be.

When they are able to walk they go to see the overarchivist in their bright, paper-walled office. The overarchivist looks at them with an expression of benevolence and ill-disguised pity, and offers them a place: cleaning, administrative work;

"The service will take care of you."

And the archivist laughs in their face, so absurd is this idea. They cannot stay among their former siblings, a charity case, an object lesson. They thank the overarchivist and leave with as much dignity as they can muster, to silence, to the step-click-scrape of their crutch and their dragging leg.

***

Re-entering society is difficult. There are some things they like, like growing their hair out and wearing everyday clothes that show off their figure, eating junk food. But none of this mitigates the gaping hole in their mind. They cannot stop feeling around it as one tongues the space left by a missing tooth. Perhaps they are hoping to notice the hole beginning to close, but they do not, it does not.

So now they go about and try to remember the combination for their bicycle lock, where they put their keys, things they've never had to put effort into before, and it is hard and sometimes they cannot do it. They create lists, on scraps of paper and napkins and scribbled in ballpoint on their hand, lists of digital bulleted lists. It's not the same. They can no longer recall the colour of Freyja's eyes.

They move to a new place, an apartment the archival service has arranged for them. It feels as though they've left a part of themself behind in the monastery, and in the rest stop, and in that hospital room, broken wet red and filmy grey pieces of them left to dry out in bedpans or half-buried in clinging sand.

They still retain a number of memories: interviews, lexicons and storytellings and other, more personal recollections, but those are fading daily, no longer crystalline, and the idea that there is no way to preserve them makes the archivist desperately sad.

They are terrified of losing everything, that their whole past will become a black hole. It's like going around without their clothes, without their skin, something they never anticipated and could never have prepared for losing.

***

It is their neighbor, Viv, who brings them back into the world. Viv is a director and (self-titled) avant-garde pornographer. She's quick to laugh and likes to sit topless on her balcony. She has blonde hair.

The archivist's own hair is growing out, dry; they don't know how to care for it. One afternoon a bottle of expensive collagen shampoo appears on their doormat:

Your ends will thank me, it read, *Viv @ 302.*

Viv shows the archivist too how to apply makeup, how to pick clothes the right colour for their skin tone. How to make tapenade. They go out and Viv buys them a coffee, the next week, a beer. Viv takes the archivist to an independent film screening, not one of her ones but something by a student at MCAD, spare and jarring and projected onto the bottom of a swimming pool. It makes the archivist feel uncomfortable in a way they want to feel again.

They go back to Viv's apartment, two floors up from the archivist's. It's got fewer walls inside than the archivist's does and everything is painted white. It reminds them sharply, again, of their little room in the monastery, and they feel an intense homesickness that Viv mistakes for shyness.

But this new world they live in has no room for homesickness or shyness so the archivist makes themself make the first move, kissing Viv on the side of her mouth, tentatively, as she turns back from a kitchen cabinet, wine bottle in hand.

Viv's bed is larger and softer than any the archivist has ever slept in. Viv, perhaps because of her profession, doesn't show any trepidation as to the nature of the archivist's genitals; she takes it all in stride. Their coupling is bittersweet because the archivist knows that the memory of it will fade, just like everything else. Just like Freyja.

The archivist is thinking of getting a job, something part-time or freelance to supplement their pension from the service. Viv tells them to enjoy their freedom,

"If you want to save money, just move in with me."

They are pleasantly surprised to find no reason to refuse. It is the biggest decision they have ever made on their own, and they are thrilled and terrified.

At the monastery they all drank only water, juice or tea, and though the archivist has drunk rice wine, raki, Chilean chardonnay, Coors lite, on their travels to make their hosts and subjects feel at ease, they have never had more than one or two in a sitting. Now though, drinking is regular and fun and their tolerance is going up. They go out in the evenings with Viv and her artistic friends, and now that they don't have data to worry about disrupting, they can – they do – black out with impunity.

"Why do you still have this?"

Viv is doing the ironing. She is holding the archivist's old smock, the only reminder of the monastic life they've managed to keep.

"I still wear them sometimes."

"You shouldn't. You should let go of the past."

"Just as pajamas."

"Even still." She balls it up and leaves the room with it. The archivist hears the door open and shut and a distant whump. Viv comes back without the smock.

"What did you do with it?"

"I put it in the chute."

"The garbage chute?"

Viv nods and then speaks, slowly and looking up through her lashes, as if penitent,

"Are you angry with me?"

"No. It's just a thing."

"I'll buy you something to make up for it."

Refusal to accept a label, male or female – for all the punishment it earned them as a child – was cultivated when the archivist entered the monastery: it was extrapolated from genderlessness out towards selflessness. At the monastery they and their peers were encouraged to give up the things that, now, people are telling them they must have: a name, a past, a favourite ice cream flavour, a gender.

Viv tries to get the archivist to pick a name,

"I don't know what to call you or how to talk about you when you're not around."

The archivist is taken aback,

"I didn't realise it was a problem."

"Well it is. It's embarrassing."

She starts referring to them as Archie to their friends. The archivist decides it's easier not to argue. It's a small sacrifice to placate Viv, and they are accustomed to sacrifice.

One day, Viv brings home a camera, turns it on as they are preparing for bed,

"Say cheese."

The archivist closes their bathrobe, tying it shut,

"Viv, what is that? I'm –" they stammer, stop, swallow, trying to get the words out and not understanding why it is so difficult. Their heart begins to beat more quickly, a muscle memory of fear, and they bite out the words: "I'm not going to be in one of your films."

But Viv is very persuasive. She pours them both a glass of wine and while they talk the archivist can feel themself being convinced. They want to agree. It's easier to go along with it, even though they had thought they'd made up their mind. This is how, the archivist thinks, she talks to clients, to investors. To arts funding bodies. Is it also how she talks to lovers?

After they are finished in the white-draped studio space the archivist feels exposed. Even after they've opened up the futon where they insist they will sleep tonight, alone. They wish for the first time in a year that they had kept the lease on their apartment.

They feel as naked as when their memory was stripped away, as times before that, before they entered the service. A very old rawness, almost forgotten, has come back. It makes them want to sink into the floor or hurt themself or at least stay in bed all week.

They ask Viv to delete the footage. Viv stands before them, still naked, holding the camera in one hand, her face unreadable. She doesn't speak for a very long time, then,

"Okay."

***

The next month Viv takes the archivist to a screening. There's a red carpet and they get front row seats, and the archivist buys a dress for the occasion, spending a month's worth of their pension all at once. It's backless, and shows off the scar that still has not faded all the way, the scar that Viv likes to run her hands over and over as they make love.

The lights go down and the first shot is of a room that feels familiar, and before the archivist can be annoyed they can't remember where they saw it they realise it's the film from that night.

They freeze, humiliation hollowing out their stomach. They are sitting in the front row, watching themself participate in an act they don't quite remember agreeing to. They have never before been the one on screen, the one recorded, archived, and they are overtaken by a repulsion so strong it makes them feel sick.

They watch themself respond to Viv's touch under the eye of the camera, analysing without meaning to the bare facts of the encounter. No watcher would believe they were reluctant: on camera they come off as eager. The inaccuracy of this impression offends their archivist's sense, sets their skin crawling. They try and fail to take refuge in righteous anger.

They are flayed. Even though their face is blurred in the footage they know everyone knows it is them. Their body shape, and the scar that they in their vanity decided to show off, are too distinctive. The eyes in the room pin them to their hard white plastic chair, strip away the makeup and Mugler gown as the archivist tries to feign nonchalance, tries not to let on that inside they are panicking, that they didn't know this was going to happen.

They try and succeed at taking refuge in the spumante being poured freely by faceless robotic waiters in every corner of the room. They rejoin Viv and a knot of her fans, fresh glass in hand, swaying on their heels. Viv half-turns, gestures at the archivist,

"— and you can see why I had to do it. Isn't she beautiful?"

The archivist throws their wine into Viv's face and walks out of the room. In the silence that follows them like a wake, the dragging scrape-step of their left leg is very loud.

They order a car with the phone Viv convinced them to buy. They cry in the back seat and the driver hands them a box of tissues and turns up the radio.

They go back to the apartment and pack up their things, grateful to the monastery for their upbringing; they have always needed very few possessions.

They have indeed been saving on rent since moving in with Viv and they can afford a hotel for a few days before they have to try and find a new place. They try not to think about the fact that they have no friends in the city who are not Viv's friends.

They wake up the next morning with a scratchy-eyed vertiginous hangover and weep salty dehydrated tears in the hotel bed because a weight has been lifted; they feel safer and freer than they have in months.

***

They decide to grow their beard out, to dye their hair, and to get a job. They're feeling stifled and tense in Boston and don't like seeing Viv's friends around the place. One humid evening, as they are sitting in their tiny, considerably cheaper apartment in Dorchester, a job opening appears on their feed, from a service they forgot they'd signed up to. It's manual archival work, digitising one of the last paper libraries in Northern California.

When, after hundreds of questionnaires and tens of video interviews and even more waiting, they get the job, they begin to cry; they don't notice until fat drops of tears fall onto the sentence they've been reading, distorting the text.

It turns out to be cheaper to rent a car and drive across-country than it is to fly. They scroll through their route, planned to the hour, and with a jolt see that it will take them through North Platte and the rest stop. It is the most direct route, a different route would cost them more than flying. It is smarter to drive.

An hour outside Pittsburgh, their phone begins to ring. It's Viv. She's called a few times since the breakup and they've had a couple of pained conversations that have come to nothing. The archivist tosses the phone out of the car window.

They drive west through a vast landscape, alternately bright and shaded with shifting clouds. It pours, dries, the car is buffetted by a windstorm and they have to turn on lateral thrusters to keep from crashing or flipping over. The windows are useless in a dust storm and they are forced to switch to instruments. Sand blasts the car in a brown static that ceases, after four hours, as abruptly as it began.

The shapes of former agricultural fields stretch away

periodically to their left and right, indefinitely, and the archivist imagines a vast empty brown patchwork covering the whole country. Occasionally they pass a farmhouse, long since abandoned, that has not yet fallen down in a storm. Once, they pass a field in which machines are overturning the earth, treating it with something, and the rich loamy smell of compost fills the car. There are placards at each corner with the governmental seal on them but they are driving too fast to read. The idea of something growing out here makes them feel giddy and lonely.

They check in at the rest stop, long-haired and made-up and unrecognisable, rumpled after their journey and looking forward to a few hours rest. A new incarnation of the person who passed through two years ago. They pass between two buildings on an enclosed walkway and catch a glimpse of some piping, the gnarled underside of the polished white station. It all looks more prosaic in the daytime but their heart begins hammering nonetheless. Their hands tighten on the railing and they force themself to look at it, to confront the rust and nickel-plating, and wait for their breathing to slow.

There's a break in the clouds and the waiting area is filled with golden light and dancing motes of dust. They warm behind the glass and the smell of their body rises; they should really use one of the showers here before they leave. They can smell warm sweat and then it comes to them, the crystal-clear memory of a pair of bodies intertwining, sun catching in downy golden hair, Freyja's blue eyes open wide with ecstasy.

Letter To My Future Lover

Laura Bridgeman

Dear Future Lover,

My body is cut.
I have 3 lines on me that you can touch.
That you can feel but you may not open.
Not from the outside.
But from the inside, through the seams of me, it may be possible.

There are other scars of course.
Love scars from other lovers (some of these I have told you about).
There are too many scars.

Scars upon scars. Like trapped people inside me. Soft lines. Little screams.

Ms Davis did the first incision. In March, a day before my dad's birthday. I was poorly. I had fibroids bearing down on me. Filling my body. Leaching my blood (I was anaemic). I was out of breath, fatigued, weak. My womb was as big as an 18 week pregnancy. In Tuke Ward, Ms Davis put me on her couch. She pushed me and prodded me. Then she ordered an MRI, a blood test and an iron transfusion. My fibroids were inside my womb. In the lining. Ms Davis offered to perform a myomectomy. But she preferred to remove the whole thing.

"I don't need my womb," I said. "I'm nearly 50."

"Some women still want theirs."

"Why?"

Ms Davis shrugged.

"Femaleness."

I didn't laugh. But I didn't say how little the word meant to me. 'Woman'. Or how disposable femaleness felt to me. How insignificant. Like ash from an e-cigarette. A womb and periods were things I could have always lived without. Always. If I'd only had a choice (if any of us did). About anatomy.

Ms Davis was ready to perform the first cut.

Strip my body of its baby-making possibility.

"Gasp."

The day of surgery, I put on the gown. The nurse weighed me. The anaesthetist shook my hand. Took my blood pressure. Asked me how I might respond to treatment. Then he wheeled me into a tiny room. 4 nurses surrounded me. The anaesthetist pricked my arm. I took the shot and went under.

In theatre, Ms Davis cut me low.

Through me. Into me. Beneath my abdomen.

"Your bikini line," she called it.

Ms Davis cut me 8 inches to take out my womb. She did well. She cut me cleanly. Then she cut me again. 1 inch. She had to. The fibroid against my bladder was so big. Ms Davis stitched me up. I came round to a morphine drip and the news that my heart rate was slow.

"Like an athlete," Ms Davis said.

"But I'm not..."

"Maybe you should be."

So I lay there with 9 inches. Courtesy of the NHS. 9 inches. There. Across my bikini line. Which is more like a Y-front line. Because I wear these. (Not that Ms Davis ever knew.) This scar cuts my body from hip bone to hip bone. And it rises up at one side like a smile. It's a friendly scar. It is also my first.

You can visit it, if you want to.

Many times.
With your hand or your mouth.

My other 2 scars are fresher.

They were made 6 months later. These scars are higher. Brighter. They are still pink. They frame my chest; they make it. Mr Barry did these. And they cost me. I went all the way to Harley Street.

"Do you want to transition?" Mr Barry said.

"I'm non-binary," I said. "Gender Queer."

"I see."

"I don't have a womb. And I don't want tits."

I told Mr Barry about my hysterectomy, I told Mr Barry how tired I was, of being in a body that betrayed me. A body that wasn't mine. I kept it light. Magical. I told Mr Barry about when I was young. How I was flat-chested. Skinny. Constantly moving. Climbing trees, dipping rivers, scaling walls. If only I could have always stayed that way. Raggedy and free.

Mr Barry smiled. Then he sent me away. To get a certificate. I went to see Dr Curtain. Just to check. Just to see whether I would have any regrets. To find out why I wanted chest surgery. Lose my breasts. Dr Curtain looked at me. He asked my height and weight. He didn't understand that I was non-binary. He kept talking to me about transition.

"I'll get you Testosterone," he said.

I didn't tell Dr Curtain, I was using T. Just a little. In pea size squirts. A friend had given me their surplus supply of Testim. To give me a lift. I put it in my thigh and biceps. My muscles grew a little and I got more energy. But I didn't want to take it full-time. Dr Curtain kept pressing me about testosterone. About people 'like me' coming to see him. About not committing either way. Then he talked to me about David Bowie.

As if I looked like him – I wish!

Eventually, Dr Curtain gave me a certificate. I went back to Mr Barry. He cut me. He slit me from the middle of my ribs, to the edge of them. 8 inches each. Mr Barry cut me cleanly. I asked him to shave down my nipples. Make them smaller. Mr Barry told me he'd place them 2 ½ centimetres above my scars. Opposite my biceps.

"Not your armpits," he said.

In Harley Street, a second anaesthetist put me under. I sank like sediment. After 5 hours, I came round. In a small room, on the ground floor. 2 drains running from me. They were empty. I was lying in the bed, looking at the ceiling. Then, I tapped my chest for the first time. My body ended where it always should have. And I grinned like I would never stop.

My chest scars are healing (I had a lot of swelling). Every day, I rub silicone into them. They fade. They gash my body. They line me. When I touch these lines, I feel my heart. Roar. Sing.

These 2 scars you can visit with your hand.

And your mouth, also.

Only if you want to.

I have 3 scars.

This is what I wanted you to know.

Next, I will write about how I want to touch you.

This is clear for me.

It's always this way.

About our Contributors

\ Gray Crosbie

Gray is a queer writer and performer who often writes in the boundary between flash-fiction and poetry. Their writing has been published in journals such as *Firewords Quarterly*, *Northwords Now* and *Litro*. In their free time, they enjoy travelling, drag shows and too many vegan donuts. www.mcrosbie.com

\ Robert Stirrups

Robert is a freelance writer whose work has appeared in over a dozen medical journals. He is currently working on a collection of short stories and has been participating in NaNoWriMo for the last decade. He has an MSc in Cognitive Science and lives just outside Edinburgh with his partner and young daughter.

\ Sarah Spence

Sarah is a PhD researcher at the University of Glasgow, specialising in the Medical Humanities. Her current project examines stigmatised health issues (mental illness, drug addiction, obesity) in contemporary Scottish literature. She writes poetry, short fiction and nonfiction and is an editor for the literary journal *From Glasgow to Saturn*. Her work appears in a variety of publications, such as *Thistle Magazine*, *The Glasgow Review of Books*, *Hold My Purse*, *Gilded Dirt*, *theGIST* and *Qmunicate*. She often writes about illness, science, history and animals. [Twitter] @_sspence

\ Harry Mason

Harry grew up writing pretentious angsty poetry and went on to get a degree in English Literature but he doesn't get to do much writing in his day job. He lives in Manchester with his wife and their mischievous cat.

\ Fee Johnstone

Fee is the Managing Editor of a medical journal and has increasingly found herself writing over the last few years. Her work has been published in the following zines: *Writer*, *Paper and Ink* and *Razur Cuts*. She placed 3rd in the Magic Oxygen Literary Prize in 2016 with *Drag Hag*.

\ Nic Lachance

Nic is a 24 year-old genderqueer who currently lives in Brighton, UK. They have recently graduated from a postgrad law degree, which turned out to be way more of a neo-colonial endeavour that bored and disenchanted them. They identify as a poet, writer, performance artist and lover. Both inspired and depressed by the world around them, they use art to find a grip on the oscillation of these experiences. They write a lot about being in a traumatised, unworthy, divine, queer, agender, ancient body and how the world feels from this perspective. A lot of their writing is centered around sex, masturbation and intimacy because they find most of their healing and teaching happens at the intersection of where our bodies meet and try to love each other past our pain. [Instragram] @nickswithpics and [Twitter] @nicooleL

\ Jonathan Bay

Jonathan is a trans poet from California currently living in Scotland as he finishes up a PhD in Creative Writing at the University of Edinburgh. He is a House of Three poet and has been published in many journals and anthologies in UK. He likes intriguingly flavourful beer, travelling to wild places and empty quiet rooms.

\ Freddie Alexander

Frederick "Freddie" Alexander is a writer and events organiser based in Edinburgh. Since 2013, he has been an organiser and host of the Inky Fingers Open Mic night and organiser of the University of Edinburgh Soapbox Open Mic. In 2014, he coordinated and hosted the second National UK University Poetry Slam. He currently works for the National Library of Scotland, and has been a freelance writer for *Broadway Baby*, *Scotsgay*, and *Gutter Magazine*. [Twitter] @FredRAlexander

\ George McDermid

George grew up in Edinburgh and started writing poetry at school, winning the Senior Poetry Prize in his 6th Year. As a teacher living in Aberdeen, he gave various readings but on leaving the north east of Scotland to chase a different career, left writing behind and has only recently returned to it. Having now moved to Fife, he very quickly re-established himself as a popular performer of his poetry, old and new, at events held at various locations throughout Fife organised by the Fife Writes Group (fifewrites.co.uk). He is now published by way of three poems in three different anthologies: *Eternal Love, Light & Darkness* and *Spring Awakening*, published by Forward Poetry. He is a founding member of 'and then the cow woke up',(andthenthecowwokeup.wordpress.com) a small group of Fife-based writers.

\ Max Scratchmann

Max is a well-known British writer and illustrator. His poems and short stories have appeared in many anthologies and magazines, and he runs the Edinburgh performance poetry company – Poetry Circus. He is the author of over thirteen books, including the award-winning autobiography about Scottish jute workers in India, *The Last Burrah Sahibs*, and the unintentionally controversial account of downshifting in the Scottish islands, *Chucking It All*. Max lives in Edinburgh and is a regular performer at the Festival Fringe as well as having been seen at the Glasgow Comedy Festival, the Imaginate Festival, the Celtic Mystery Festival, the Merchant City Festival, Kelburn Garden Party, the Hidden Door Festival and many more...

\ Iliria Osum

Iliria is 26, avoids gendered identity structures but goes by 'she/her', 'gender-expansive woman' and 'fem-aligned' when necessary, and has most recently been published in *The Adirondack Review*, *By & By*, *Strange Horizons*, and *Goblinfruit*. She was a poetry finalist in the 2017 Pinch Journal Literary Contest, and her play *What Feels To My Heart* was produced in New York in June 2017. She teaches at an alternative high school in New Jersey, and tweets, albeit rarely @iliriaosum.

\ Hannah Newell

Hannah is a London-based writer and editor. Her writing has been published in art and cultural magazines such as *PARSE* journal and *JAWS*, for whom she is a peer reviewer. In 2014, she completed a Master's degree in Critical Writing in Art and Design at the Royal College of Art. Between August 2014 and December 2016, Hannah worked as Editor at Black Dog Publishing. She is currently self-employed as a project editor of illustrated books on art and design, a web editor at the Royal College of Art and provides freelance copy-editing and proof-reading services.

\ Brook Shelley

Brook lives in Portland, OR with her cat Snorri. Her writing has appeared in *The Toast*, *Lean Out*, *Transfigure* and the *Oregon Journal of the Humanities*. She speaks at conferences on queer and trans issues, ans is co-chair of the board of Basic Rights Oregon. You can finde her on [Twitter] @brookshelley and brookshelley.com

\ Ever Dundas

Ever is a writer specialising in the weird and macabre, with Queer Theory (problematizing the 'normal') forming the backbone of her work. She writes literary fiction, sci-fi, horror, and fantasy. Her first novel, *Goblin*, won the Saltire First Book of the Year Award in 2017. She is currently working on her second novel, *HellSans*, a science fiction thriller with disability as a major theme. You can find her on [Twitter] @everdundas, [Facebook] @EverRADundas and everdundas.com

\ Oliver Geffers/Samanta Bellevue

Oliver AKA Samanta was born in Kiel, Germany. He spent his childhood in Mons near Brussels, Belgium. Since 2004 he lives in Bonn, Germany where he works as an LGBTQ activist, interpreter, consultant and journalist.

\ Ely Percy

Ely is a Scottish fiction writer, a memoirist and an epistolarian. Their first work *Cracked: Recovering From Traumatic Brain Injury* (JKP, 2002) took the form of both a creative and an academic text; they graduated with distinction from Glasgow University's Mphil in Creative Writing in 2004, and since then their work has appeared in many reputable literary journals such as *The Edinburgh Review*, *The Scotsman Orange*, *New Writing Scotland* and *Causeway*. Over the last 15 years, Percy has facilitated countless writing workshops for various minority groups; they've been writer-in-residence in a prison, edited a lesbian publication and worked as a community librarian in an LGBT centre. They are currently writer-in-residence at Cradle vegan cafe.

\ D Bruton

D is a teacher in a high-school in Scotland. He hopes he is a teacher that the children will talk about fondly when they are grown up and remembering. He writes, too, because he has stories in his head. Sometimes his stories have something to say, about life and love and universal compassion – and those are his best stories. He has been published in many nice places and by good people including *Brittle Star Magazine*, *The Irish Literary Review*, Fiction Attic Press and Freight Books.

\ Tanisha Catt

Tanisha is an Editorial Assistant for children's magazines and a graduate in Creative Writing, Journalism and English at the University of Strathclyde. She was born and raised in Scotland, and spends her time making content – be it comics, short stories, or animations. She describes her life as 'a series of nonsense', and it often shows in her work. Her strength can be found in proofreading, while her weakness can be found in Battenberg cake.

\ Julya Oui

Julya is an author and a screenwriter who believes in keeping monsters, having nightmares, and dreaming up worlds that defy logic. While Mother Nature inspires her, mindbending curiosities motivate her. She lives in a town known as the City of Everlasting Peace, or Taiping, somewhere north of Malaysia. She is also a pluviophile and an entomophile who loves shinrin-yoku.

\ Eris Young

Eris is a queer and trans writer from California. They moved to Edinburgh three years ago for the lit scene and, apparently, the damp. Their work is primarily concerned with using speculative fiction to challenge the status quo and explore LGBTQ themes. Their fiction has been featured in *Scrutiny Journal*, *Bewildering Stories* and *Esoterica Magazine*.

\ Laura Bridgeman

Bridgeman has written for the theatre and BBC Radio 4 and has a PhD from UEA in Creative Writing where they were awarded the HSC Scholarship. Their novel, *Raphael Coombs*, was short-listed for the Charles Pick Fellowship. Bridgeman currently teaches Creative Writing at Queen Mary University and Imperial University. They have taught in 5 UK prisons. They also run their own press – hotpencil – with Serge Nicholson. Their publications include: *There Is No Word For It, The (Trans) Mangina Monologues* (2011) and *The Butch Monologues* (2017). *The Butch Monologues* is currently on a sell-out UK tour, funded by The Arts Council of England (2017).

Enormous gratitude to Pace Gallery and the artists Natalie Frank and Kiki Smith for their thought-provoking artwork and generosity.

The art is featured in Hannah Newell's essay *Hairy on the Inside*.

About Knight Errant Press

Knight Errant Press are here to champion you — readers and writers — and to carry your voices, loud and proud, out into the world.

We want you to find the courage and inspiration, through writing and the gut-punching power of words, to become your own Knight in Shining Armour. Here we will armour you and your peers with the knowledge that difference is precious, essential and must be fought for and defended in these troublesome times.

We may be small but we are mighty! We believe that the English language, the almighty global tycoon, despite its reputation, can serve some good in uniting people from the most unlikely places and diverse backgrounds.

We look forward to publishing a variety of creations — but especially pieces that challenge literary genres and norms and address the need for intersectional thinking and writing in today's world. Our aim is to bring about more narratives from and about LGBTQIA, BAME and migrant folk into Scotland and the wider UK, as well as be the bridge into English for similar narratives from other cultures and languages by supporting translators and publishing works and authors in translation.

These voices often slip past the big yins and are deemed too niche for commercial publishing. We are willing to take the risk. For as the artist and letter-writer, Vincent van Gogh, once wrote:

The fishermen know that the sea is dangerous and the storm terrible, but they have never found these dangers sufficient reason for remaining ashore.

No human experience, fictional or otherwise, is too niche for us. We love writing that challenges preconceived notions and makes us think and probe beyond our elaborately constructed realities. We hope to nourish such talent at Knight Errant.

It is our mission to make your voices heard, read and recognised.

We are still a fledgling press, launched in March 2017 and run by a bunch of risk-taking freelancers.

Find out more about us at knighterrantpress.com

Submissions

Knight Errant Press accepts unsolicited submissions both from unrepresented writers and agents.

We are particularly interested in short fiction and small books:

Short stories

Novellas and novelettes

Flash fiction

We also accept novels, poetry collections, narrative non-fiction, essays and graphic narratives. We are tentative but curious to foray into children's and YA.

You must be over 16 to submit your work to us. If you are younger than 18 we will require parental consent to publish.

To find out more about our Submission Guidelines, please visit us at knighterrantpress.com

They Come from Within

Writing Workshops

Our aim as a publisher is to nourish and amplify voices and tales from the margins. We are passionate about creating more accessible opportunities for creatives. Setting up a writing workshop to help grow and inspire local writers felt like a natural step to make.

We aim to create a safe and welcoming space for writers of all abilities and inclinations. Whether you are a seasoned veteran, an occasional scribbler or someone who is just starting out – you are welcome.

We, as well as your workshop peers, will help you develop and nourish your ideas and words. We also offer the opportunity to receive feedback – both peer and professional.

Our objectives:

1) to provide a friendly and safe environment for writers of all levels of experience and from all walks of life to have a space to practice, develop and improve their craft and share it with like-minded folk

2) accessible – all skill levels and forms of writing welcome

3) free, no fees – donation based , pay what you can (to cover costs of materials and guest tutors, space hire is usually free)

4) inclusive – with a focus on promoting both writers from and those who write about (or both) the LGBTQI, ethnic minorites, migration stories, words in translation and such; allies welcome

5) honest, compassionate and supportive environment, no cut-throat competition

6) professional and peer feedback

7) flexibility – we will improve and revise our workshops based on your feedback and suggestions

For the latest events, visit us at knighterrantpress.com [Workshops] or follow us on social media: [Facebook] @knighterrantpress and [Twitter] @knighterrantpub

Volume 2...

You got this far, congratulations!

We have our eyes set on the end of 2018 for Volume 2 of #QueerQuarrels.

We've a solid 2/3 of the content ready but, having split the anthology into two books, there is room for more and we are currently on the look-out for more writing, poetry and art to fill the pages of the next volume.

Have a #quarrel brewing inside you?

Know someone who might?

Drop us a line at knighterrantpress @ outlook. com

(It doesn't have to be complete, we're happy to work with a pitch.)

Our hard deadline is the 1st of September 2018.

Essay References

Hairy on the Inside (Hannah Newell)

Beard, M. (2017). "Women in Power". *London Review of Books*. (Vol 39, No 6). pp 9 – 14.

de Beauvoir, S. (2010). *The Second Sex*. London:Vintage.

Carter, A. (2006). *The Bloody Chamber and Other Stories*. Kindle ed. London: Vintage.

Cixous, H. (1976). *The Laugh of Medusa*. Translated by Keith Cohen and Paula Cohen. *Signs* (Vol 1, No 4). Chicago: University of Chicago Press. pp 875 – 993.

Kraus, C. (2015). *I Love Dick*. Kindle ed. London:Tuskar Rock Press.

Shiach, M. (1991). *A Politics of Writing*. London and NewYork: Routledge.

Reilly, M. ed. (2015). *Women Artists: The Linda Nochlin Reader*. London: Thames and Hudson.

Discography

Foad, P., Hammond, P., Munro, J. and Woods, L. (2006) *Stepping Out of Line*. Chessington: Catsle, Ltd.

Authenticated Author (Ever Dundas)

Abdel-Magied,Y. (2016). *As Lionel Shriver made light of identity, I had no choice but to walk out on her'*. *The Guardian*, [online]. Available at: https://www.theguardian.com/commentisfree/2016/sep/10/as-lionel-shriver-made-light-of-identity-i-had-no-choice-but-to-walk-out-on-her [Accessed 30 Oct. 2017].

Butler, J. (1999). *Gender Trouble: Feminism and the Subversion of Identity*. 2nd ed. NewYork: Routledge.

Dazai, O (1993). *Blue Bamboo*. London: Kodansha Europe Ltd.

Delaney, B. (2016). "They called me the antichrist": JT LeRoy, Laura Albert *and the literary hoax. The Guardian, [online]. Available at: https://www. theguardian.com/film/2016/dec/28/they-called-me-the-antichrist-jt-leroy-laura-albert-and-the-six-year-literary-hoax [Accessed 30 Oct. 2017].*

Eddo-Lodge, R. (2017). Why I'm No Longer Talking To White People About Race. London: Bloomsbury Publishing.

Ellis-Petersen, H. (2015) Male writers continue to dominate literary criticism, Vida study finds. The Guardian, [online]. Available at: https://www. theguardian.com/books/2015/apr/07/male-writers-continue-dominate-literary-criticism-vida-study-finds [Accessed 30 Oct. 2017].

Flood, A. (2014). Judy Blume: "I thought, this is America: we don't ban books. But then we did". The Guardian, [online]. Available at: https://www. theguardian.com/books/2014/jul/11/judy-blume-interview-forever-writer-children-young-adults [Accessed 30 Oct. 2017].

Galbraith, R. (2013). The Cuckoo's Calling. 1st ed. London: Sphere.

Galbraith website. 'About: FAQ'. [online]. Available at: http://robert-galbraith.com/about/ [Accessed 30 Oct. 2017].

Gamble, S. (2006). Angela Carter: A Literary Life. Hampshire: Palgrave Macmillan.

Haraway, D.J. (1991). A Cyborg Manifesto: Science, Technology, and Socialist-Feminism in the Late Twentieth Century in Simians, Cyborgs, and Women. London: Free Association Books.

Harrison, M.I. (2012). Writing Characters of the Opposite Gender. [online] Intergalactic Medicine Show. Available at: http://www. intergalacticmedicineshow.com/cgi-bin/mag.cgi?do=columns&vol=mette_ivie_harrison&article=044 [Accessed: 30 Oct. 2017].

Hoyle, B. (2007). Revenge of the bloodthirsty lesbians. The Times, [online]. Available at: https://www.thetimes.co.uk/article/revenge-of-the-bloodthirsty-lesbians-tqk5rjv7hpz [Accessed 30 Oct. 2017].

Kunzru, H. et al. (2016). Whose life is it anyway? Novelists have their say on cultural appropriation. The Guardian, [online]. Available at: https://www. theguardian.com/books/2016/oct/01/novelists-cultural-appropriation-literature-lionel-shriver [Accessed 30 Oct. 2017].

MacCormack, P. (2006). The Great Ephemeral Tattooed Skin, Body and Society, 12(2), pp64.

O'Connell, A. (2004). Fresh Orange. The Times, [online]. Available at: https://www.thetimes.co.uk/article/fresh-orange-qsf5jlrh87w [Accessed 30 Oct. 2017].

Perry, S. (2017). Sarah Perry Discusses Not Being a Woman Writer. [online]. Writers and Artists. Available at: https://www.writersandartists.co.uk/writers/advice/686/a-writers-toolkit/story-and-plot/ [Accessed 30 Oct. 2017].

Plath, S. (1999). Letters Home: Correspondence 1950-1963. Faber: London.

Prose, F. (1998). Scent of a Woman's Ink: Are women writers really inferior? [online]. Harpers. Available at: https://harpers.org/archive/1998/06/scent-of-a-womans-ink/ [Accessed 30 Oct. 2017].

Prose, F. (2011). On Women Writers and V.S. Naipaul. [online]. Harpers. Available at: https://harpers.org/blog/2011/06/on-women-writers-and-v-s-naipaul/ [Accessed 30 Oct. 2017].

Reference. (n.d.) Queer. In: Oxford Dictionaries Thesaurus [online]. Available at: https://en.oxforddictionaries.com/thesaurus/queer [Accessed 30 Oct. 2017].

Sensel, J. (2009). [Blog] Gender and Perception. The Spectacle blog. Available at: http://web.archive.org/web/20091124210644/thespectacleblog.wordpress.com/2009/11/10/gender-and-perception/ [Accessed: 30 Oct. 2017].

Serano, J. (2017). Debunking "Trans Women Are Not Women" Arguments. [online]. Medium. Available at: https://medium.com/@juliaserano/debunking-trans-women-are-not-women-arguments-85fd5ab0e19c [Accessed 30 Oct. 2017].

Shriver, L. (2016). Lionel Shriver's full speech: "I hope the concept of cultural appropriation is a passing fad". The Guardian, [online]. Available at: https://www.theguardian.com/commentisfree/2016/sep/13/lionel-shrivers-full-speech-i-hope-the-concept-of-cultural-appropriation-is-a-passing-fad [Accessed 30 Oct. 2017].

Smith, M. (2017) Casting a woman as the Doctor isn't clever, it's sad and predictable. The Herald. [online] Available at: http://www.heraldscotland.com/news/15414330.Mark_Smith__Casting_a_woman_as_the_Doctor_isn_t_clever__it_s_sad_and_predictable/ [Accessed: 30 Oct. 2017].

Stroumboulopoulos, G. (2012) Gorge R.R. Martin: Full Extended Interview. [online]. CBC. Available at: http://www.cbc.ca/strombo/videos/george-rr-martin-full-extended-interview [Accessed 30 Oct. 2017].

Vidaweb, (2016). The 2015 VIDA Count. Available at: http://www.vidaweb.org/the-2015-vida-count [Accessed 30 Oct. 2017].

Wade, M. (2010). Louise Welsh: "I want people to feel things." The Times, *[online]. Available at: https://www.thetimes.co.uk/article/louise-welsh-i-want-people-to-feel-things-v07j70t56kh [Accessed 30 Oct. 2017].*

Weigel, M. (2016) Political correctness: how the right invented a phantom enemy. The Guardian [online] Available at: https://www.theguardian.com/us-news/2016/nov/30/political-correctness-how-the-right-invented-phantom-enemy-donald-trump [Accessed 30 Oct. 2017].

Twelve Years A Slave and Racism in the UK (2014). [Blog] How Upsetting. Available at: https://howupsetting.com/2014/01/09/12-years-a-slave-and-racism-in-the-uk/ [Accessed 30 Oct. 2017].

Supreme Human Beings
who helped make this happen

Jamie Graham
Sara Davis
Olga Pinchuk
Chris Bache
Christina Castelli
Annette Hayes
Kjell Mohr
Lenka Murová
Cordula Hallensleben
Laura Clements
Nathan Gale
REEKperfume
Peter Strömberg
James Morton
Pax Lowey
George McDermid
D Bruton
Darach Miller
Sarah Nguyen
Ralph Dunn
Simon Eilbec
Greg Shocklee
Fee Johnstone
Lighthouse Books
Kirsty Hunter
Pete Mowat
Regina Lipp
Tiff Ferentini

Ash Meyer
Ari Golding
Ari Smith
Bex Hughes
C M Parry
Shelly Nobbs
Soatikee D. Driver
Ewen McNeill
penwing
Matt Asher Peralta
Nathan Oliver Pedersen
Gustaf Rydevik
GMarkC
Sarah E M Mason
Michelle Dalton
Vivian
Marinca
Dr Evangeline Tsao
Mark Brindley
Michael Bacon
Cara Moon
Laura Clay
Sam Boyce
CN Lester
Jonathan Bay
Rok Nežic
SamLR
Katharina Roeder

CuriosityRocks
Essei Barcroft
Lisa MacKenzie
Sophie Pinkoski
Miceala Shocklee
Roberta Balfour
Tasha Turner
Lord Emry's Oswin Oswald
Helene Kathinka Kirkegaard
MA Creative Writing@Edinburgh Napier

Library Donations:

Catriona Cox to Killarney Public Library, Ireland
Chris Sun to Oakland Public Library, USA
Ever Dundas to Edinburgh Central Library, Scotland
Pax Lowey to Bromley House Library, England
Castlemilk Library, Scotland
Linden V Weisberg to The Seven Hills School, USA
Ely Percy to Outhouse East, England
Samantha Piszkiewicz to LGBT Center of Raleigh, USA
Antonia Layzell to Sudbury Library, England